D1133532

An Introduction to
CLOUD FOREST TREES:
Monteverde, Costa Rica

by William A. Haber, Willow Zuchowski,
and Erick Bello

Illustrated by Willow Zuchowski

Cover: *Pithecellobium costaricense* (*Cojoba costaricensis*)

Authors and illustrator may be contacted at:

Apdo. 50-5655
Monteverde, Costa Rica

582.16
H-114i Haber, William A.
        An Introduction to Cloud Forest Trees:
        Monteverde, Costa Rica/William A. Haber,
        Willow Zuchowski, Erick Bello Carranza;
        il. por Willow Zuchowski. - - 1. ed.- -
        San José, Costa Rica: La Nación, 1996

        204 p.: il.; 22 cm

        ISBN 9968–759–03–1

        1. Arboles – Monteverde. 2. Bosques – Costa
Rica. I. Zuchowski, Willow. II. Bello Caranza,
Erick. III. Título.

Impresión Comercial, La Nación S.A.

ACKNOWLEDGMENTS

We are especially grateful to several dozen plant taxonomists who have consistently provided expert identifications of our specimens over the years and worked with us to solve numerous problems with species that look alike and with plants that have no names. We also thank the many landowners in the Monteverde region who permitted us to collect plant specimens from their remaining forest tracts, especially the Monteverde Conservation League, the Tropical Science Center, and the families of John Campbell, Wolf Guindon and Joe Stuckey. We are grateful for Peter Raven's continual support and encouragement for the Monteverde flora project over the years. Our colleagues in Costa Rican botany, Barry Hammel and Mike Grayum, were essential to many aspects of the production of this book. Costa Rican botanists, Luis Diego Gómez, Jorge Gómez-Lorito, Quírico Jiménez, Luis Poveda, Pablo Sánchez, and Nelson Zamora not only helped us to identify plants, but shared their warehouse of information about the Costa Rican flora. The personnel of the National Biodiversity Institute (INBio) and the Department of Natural History at the National Museum of Costa Rica, (where the National Herbarium is housed) were continuously helpful with access to their plant collections and library resources. We are also grateful to Cecilia Herrera, who typed over 15,000 plant labels into the computer database at INBio.

We also appreciate the efforts of another group of our colleagues who critically read and edited the manuscript; these include Glenn Adelson, Michael & Patricia Fogden, Mike Grayum, Carlos Guindon, Barry Hammel, Frank Joyce, Sharon Kinsman, Alan and Karen Masters, Greg Murray, Dan Perlman, Carlos de la Rosa, and Jim Wolfe. Eladio Cruz, Chris Ivey, Wolf Guindon and Darin Penneys provided expert assistance in the field at many stages during the project.

Financial support for our field work was provided by the Missouri Botanical Garden, the National Geographic Society, the Portland Nature Conservancy, and the J. L. Miller family of St. Louis. The Tropical Science Center helped finance the publication.

CONTENTS

PART III. Appendices 162

Index 192

vi

INTRODUCTION

This book provides an entry point for anyone, whether biologist or amateur naturalist, interested in learning about the trees of the Monteverde area and how to identify them. The goal of the book is to give Monteverde visitors a brief introduction to the woody vegetation of the area, to aid in the identification of the most common and conspicuous species, and to offer basic information about their natural history, such as patterns of distribution, pollination mechanisms, and adaptations for seed dispersal. The area covered by the book extends from the village of Santa Elena at 1250 m through the community of Monteverde and the Monteverde Cloud Forest Preserve up to the Continental Divide at 1600 m, and the emergent peaks that reach 1845 m.

Part I, Chapter 1 provides basic information about the geography, climate and soils of the Monteverde region. Chapter 2 offers an overview of vegetation types, patterns of species distribution and biodiversity. Chapter 3 discusses several aspects of tree natural history at Monteverde.

Part II is the identification guide. Chapter 4 includes a short discussion about useful methods and techniques for studying trees, while Chapter 5 provides some simple keys to species groups and a description of each of the species treated in the book along with information about its distribution, abundance, similar species, and natural history. Special family boxes, providing in-depth family characteristics and natural history, are scattered throughout the book. Groups 1 and 4 concentrate on particular families (Arecaceae and Rubiaceae).

The Appendices include a list of trees described in the book arranged by family, a checklist of all tree species found at Monteverde, trees categorized according to various characteristics, a glossary, and some useful references for finding more information.

PART I. The Monteverde Forests

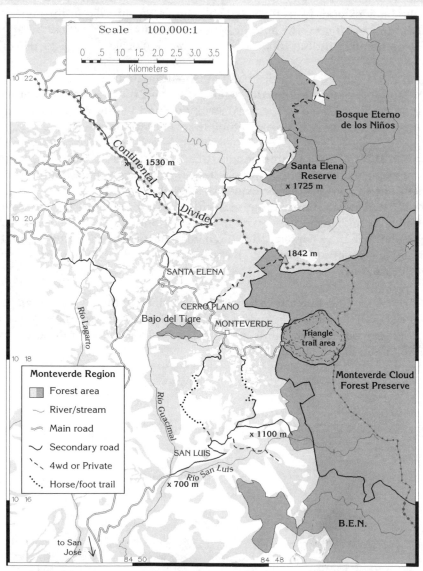

Adapted from map by David King 1996

2

Chapter 1. Geography, Climate, and Soils

GEOGRAPHY

Topography

The community of Monteverde (1350–1500 m) lies on the upper Pacific slope near the Continental Divide in the Cordillera de Tilarán (Tilarán mountain range) in northwestern Costa Rica. The nearest town is Santa Elena (1250 m), a small rural village 35 km up the gravel road from the Río Lagarto turn-off on the Inter-American Highway. The population of Santa Elena and its surrounding communities is approximately 6,500. Monteverde proper, with a population of about 250, consists of a diffuse array of dairy farms, hotels and residences spreading along a narrow plateau that drops off steeply on the southwestern side into the San Luis Valley and rises sharply on the northeastern side to the peaks and ridges of the Continental Divide.

At this point in the Cordillera, the Divide broadens into an irregular mesa with river canyons (quebradas), ridges and emergent peaks. The most notable peaks are Cerro Amigos ("friends' mountain") (1842 m) where the TV repeater towers are located, Cerro "sin nombre" ("mountain without name") (1699 m), which is crossed by the Chomogo trail in the Monteverde Cloud Forest Preserve, and Cerro Chomogo ("swamp mountain") (1799 m) located above the Estación Biológica (Canadian Biological Station).

This mountain mass serves as the source for several major rivers that flow either northeast toward the Caribbean or southwest to the Golfo de Nicoya. The main rivers on the Pacific side are the Río Guacimal, Río Lagarto, and Río Cañas. The Río San Luis joins the Guacimal at the village of San Luis (700 m) in the San Luis Valley below Monteverde. The largest rivers on the Atlantic side include the Río Chiquito and Río Caño Negro that empty into Lago Arenal and the Río Peñas Blancas that merges with several other large rivers before dumping into the Río San Juan, which forms the northeastern border between Costa Rica and Nicaragua.

Natural areas

The Monteverde Cloud Forest Preserve (10,500 hectares or 26,000 acres) straddles the Continental Divide to the north and east of the Monteverde community. Access begins at the Preserve's Information Center (La Casona), which can be reached by vehicle on an all weather road from Monteverde. The Preserve has a well-maintained trail system in the area between the Information Center (1520 m) and the Divide (1580–1600 m), and a more primitive series of trails that extend out to the far reaches of the area. The MCFP is owned and operated by the Tropical Science Center, a private, non-profit association based in San José. The **Santa Elena Reserve** (about 310 hectares or 765 acres) lies on the high Atlantic slope and Divide to the north of Monteverde and Santa Elena. It can be reached by driving north from Santa

3

Elena, turning right on the road to Las Nubes, and then following the road signs. The SER is managed by the local technical high school. The **Bajo del Tigre Reserve** (about 30 hectares or 75 acres), a sector of the Bosque Eterno de los Niños, is located on the Pacific slope adjoining the Monteverde community between the Río Guacimal and Quebrada Máquina. The entrance is between the dairy plant and CASEM, the artisans' co-op. Most of the **Bosque Eterno de los Niños** (Children's Eternal Forest) (17,000 hectares or 42,000 acres) lies to the north and east of the Monteverde Cloud Forest Preserve on the Atlantic slope, but part of it wraps around to the Pacific side of the Cordillera along the south side of the Monteverde Preserve. BEN can be reached by an overnight hike through the Monteverde Preserve into the Peñas Blancas Valley, by a horse trail into the San Gerardo Valley that starts at the SER, or by vehicle from the town of La Tigra in the Atlantic lowlands of San Carlos. BEN is owned and managed by the Monteverde Conservation League, based in Monteverde.

CLIMATE

In Costa Rica, the sunny dry season corresponding to the northern winter—December to April—is called *verano* or "summer," while the cloudy wet season—May to November—is known as *invierno* or "winter." Although the nights are much cooler than the days, the temperatures of *verano* are only slightly cooler than those of *invierno*. In fact, the clear dry season days can often feel much hotter than the cloudier, wet season days.

The main features that characterize Monteverde's climate include mild, montane temperatures, a seasonal pattern of rainfall, and the influence of strong northeast trade winds. Temperatures are distinctly cooler here overall than in the lowlands, with highs of 20–23° C. (68–73.4° F.) and lows of 9–11° C. (48.2–51.8° F.) (Figure 1).

Two main seasons occur at Monteverde—a wet season from mid-May to mid-November and a dry season that extends from mid-November through mid-May (Figure 2). Total annual rainfall at Monteverde averages about 2500 mm (98 inches), but varies greatly from year to year; records taken since 1956 range from 1715–3234 mm. The total is lower on the Pacific slope (about 2000 mm at San Luis) and higher on the mountain crest (3000 mm). The much wetter Peñas Blancas Valley (e.g., Refugio Eladio) receives as much as 7–8 m (25 feet!) of rain annually.

As experienced at ground level in Monteverde, the northeast trade winds (*alisios*) are seasonal, persisting from November to April. These winds tend to be most consistent from November through January, and then gradually diminish through April. The trade winds actually blow all year round. However, during the wet season they move at higher altitudes, being pushed upward when they meet the warm air over the Pacific land mass, and thus, they are usually not noticeable at ground level. The trade winds are especially strong at La Ventana on the Continental Divide where average wind speeds

4

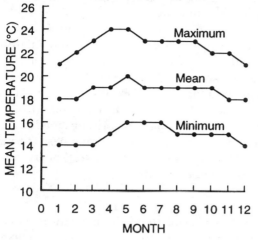

Figure 1. Mean monthly temperature at Monteverde (1961-1991). Mean annual temperature equals 18.75° C.

Source: Instituto Meteorológico Nacional.

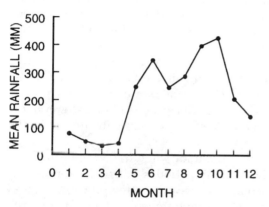

Figure 2. Mean monthly rainfall at Monteverde (1956-1992). Mean annual rainfall equals 2493 mm.

Source: Instituto Meteorológico Nacional.

of 20–40 km per hour are normal and peaks of 80–100 km/hour are not uncommon, especially during storms in January.

Wet season

Two peaks in rainfall occur during the wet season—one in June and a second during September–October (Figure 2). These peaks follow changes in the heating of the earth by the sun as it passes overhead during the march of the seasons. Between July and August a short period of about two weeks of dry weather occurs, which is often accompanied by an increase in the trade winds. This *veranillo* or "little summer" reflects a slight cooling of the land while the summer sun is over Mexico. The hurricane season extends from August through October. These storms, which develop out of low pressure areas in the Caribbean called tropical depressions, draw air from the Pacific across the mountains toward the Atlantic. When this moist air reaches the mountains, it condenses and produces cool, rainy-drizzly weather known locally as a *temporal* ("storm"). Temporales last from a few days to as long as a week or more. These are depressing periods when everything becomes damp and leather shoes turn pea-soup green with mildew.

A typical wet season day starts out calm and clear to partly cloudy. During the morning, clouds gradually build up on both the Pacific and Atlantic slopes, developing into impressive thunderheads in the early afternoon that move up the slope, progressively closing in on Monteverde. At mid-day, ground level clouds often move in like a fog bank to obscure the entire landscape, soon followed by showers. The clouds can produce anything from a light shower to a heavy tropical deluge accompanied by intense lightning. The showers are often brief, but they may be repeated several times. During the transition between seasons in May and November, the weather patterns are irregular and showers can come at almost anytime.

Dry season

From November through May very little precipitation falls in the form of rain, although one or two showers often occur in March and April as a precursor of the rainy season. The dry season is characterized by slightly cooler temperatures and the persistent trade winds that carry moist air inland from the Caribbean, driving it up the mountain slopes where it cools and condenses into clouds. The clouds regularly produce rain on the Atlantic slope, even during the dry season, and they blow across the mountain crest carrying fine to heavy mists that keep the cloud forest green. These wind-blown mists can reach well down the Pacific slope, arriving as far as the village of San Luis. However, the dry season mists affect the vegetation less as one moves further down the slope from the Continental Divide.

During November and December the trade winds and wind-borne mists are at their most intense level. Locally, this period is called "the windy-misty season." While common, these cool, misty days are often interspersed with warmer, clear weather. The mists decrease in frequency, producing progressively drier weather from January to April. During January the trade winds are sometimes reinforced by cold fronts that move down from the north producing extremely strong winds and chilly temperatures that last for several days. These cold, drizzly storms are called *nortes* (northers) or *temporales del Atlántico*. The high winds that accompany nortes often blow down trees and branches and can even tear leaves off the trees leaving the ground carpeted in green.

A typical day in February begins cool and windy with clouds driven by the trade winds scudding over the peaks and ridges of the Continental Divide. As these clouds hit the warm air rising off the sun-warmed land on the Pacific side, they quickly evaporate. By noon most of the clouds have disappeared and the sun feels warm. By mid-afternoon the clouds are blowing over the mountains again and it is chilly in the shade. At sundown, the mist is blowing in horizontal sheets across the landscape making double rainbows over the Monteverde hills.

Atlantic versus Pacific weather

The interaction between the trade winds and the mountains causes a strong difference in the seasonality of precipitation between the Atlantic and Pacific slopes. The regular wet season rains last about two months longer on the Atlantic slope (May through January) and the *veranillo* is less pronounced there. Even though a mild dry season occurs from February to April, the Atlantic slope receives rain all year. As a result, the Atlantic side receives over twice as much rainfall annually as the Pacific side. The further down the Pacific slope one goes, the drier and more seasonal the climate becomes. Near the top of the Cordillera, the climate is intermediate between the Atlantic and Pacific in seasonality. The Monteverde community is somewhat sheltered from the mists by the high peaks to the northeast. The Bajo del Tigre Reserve and the Guacimal valley below Monteverde are the most affected by this rain shadow as reflected in the drier forest found there. During Pacific *temporales* the weather often remains clear in Peñas Blancas. When *nortes* hit, it is wet and miserable on the Atlantic side, but clear, warm, and breezy on the Pacific slope.

El Niño effect

The El Niño effect (named for "the Christ-child" because its occurrence often coincides with the Christmas season) is a climatic anomaly that occurs when the cold ocean current off the South American coast veers out to sea to the west for reasons that are still poorly understood. The shift results in warmer water along the coast of Central and South America that temporarily creates warmer, drier weather. In years when El Niño is pronounced, commercial fishing and local climate can be affected from Chile to California. In Costa Rica, El Niño years have a longer dry season and a shorter, warmer and drier wet season. The change in weather commonly fools certain species of local trees into flowering six months out of their normal annual cycle.

GEOLOGY AND SOILS

The Cordillera de Tilarán consists mostly of andesite and riolite formed in volcanic eruptions and lava flows during the Tertiary period (12–60 million years ago). Most of the surface rocks are considered to be relatively young, about 3–5 million years old (Pliocene epoch). The gray sand (riolite) mined from quarries along the road to Monteverde, used for surfacing the roads and making concrete, originated from volcanic extrusion, and it is not sedimentary as many people think.

Soils of the Monteverde area are also volcanic, having developed from weathered volcanic rock and ash deposits. Where they are not badly eroded, these soils are deep and dark colored, rich in organic matter, medium textured and low to moderately fertile (with the appearance of topsoil). Where they have been heavily eroded on steeper terrain these soils are shallow, reddish, low in organic matter, heavy textured and low to very low in fertility (with the appearance of red clay).

Chapter 2. Forest Types, Biodiversity, and Distribution

OVERVIEW OF COSTA RICAN VEGETATION

Most of Costa Rica's land area was originally covered by forest vegetation. The grassy, savanna-like areas seen so commonly now along the highways have resulted from clearing by humans for agriculture and cattle ranching. These areas can only be maintained as grassland by repeated clearing and burning. Naturally open areas in Costa Rica are found on the top of Cerro Chirripó (Chirripó National Park), in marshes, and in areas where the natural vegetation has been killed by fires initiated by lightning (possibly on Cerro de la Muerte), or by volcanic activity (Poas and Arenal volcanoes).

From one place to another in Costa Rica, the type of forest cover varies greatly in height, tree density and species composition. The primary factors affecting differences in forest characteristics are 1) the amount of annual rainfall and its seasonal distribution and 2) changes in temperature associated with elevation. The vegetation of Costa Rica has been classified into 12 distinct vegetation types or **life zones** under the Holdridge system (Holdridge 1967). These life zones range from a dry, deciduous, scrubby forest in the northwest that is mostly leafless for six months of the year (e.g., Santa Rosa National Park), to 40 m tall, constantly wet, lowland rain forest of the Atlantic slope and lowlands (e.g., La Selva Biological Station and Tortuguero National Park), to oak-dominated cloud forest of the high Talamanca mountains (e.g., Cerro de la Muerte). For more detailed descriptions of Costa Rican vegetation, see Hartshorn (1983), Hartshorn and Hammel (1994), and Nadkarni and Wheelwright (1997).

VEGETATION OF THE MONTEVERDE AREA

Forest zones
Vegetation in the Monteverde area has been divided into a total of seven distinct Holdridge life zones, all of which are types of tropical evergreen forest (Tosi 1969). However, for the non-technical reader these zones may be grouped into three broad categories: 1) highly seasonal forest on the Pacific slope in the rain shadow of the Cordillera de Tilarán, 2) cloud forest on the exposed peaks and ridges along the mountain crest, and 3) very wet, almost aseasonal rain forest on the Atlantic slope. A short description of each of the three major forest types is given below with an indication of its location and importance in our area.

Pacific slope seasonal forest
A seasonally dry, though mostly evergreen forest (Premontane wet forest life zone) is found in the Monteverde community and in the watersheds of the

Guacimal and San Luis Rivers on the Pacific slope at 800–1400 m. This area receives 2–2.5 meters (6.6–8.2 feet) of rainfall annually and experiences a strong dry season from November to May when little rain falls in the form of showers. In addition, the peaks of the Cordillera to the northeast of Monteverde create a rain shadow that blocks most of the wind-borne mist that helps keep the higher areas green during the dry season. As a result, several species, e.g., *Cedrela tonduzii* (Meliaceae), *Sapium glandulosum* (Euphorbiaceae), *Styphnolobium monteviridis* (Fabaceae), lose their leaves for a month or two in the dry season. As one moves down the Pacific slope, the vegetation becomes progressively drier, reflecting the more seasonal climate, and deciduous species form an increasingly larger proportion of the canopy.

The forest has a closed canopy formed by an overstory of tall, straight trees reaching 30–40 m where they are sheltered from the wind. The trunks have bare bark with little moss and lichen cover and few species of the climbing aroids (Araceae) and cyclanths (Cyclanthaceae) that are abundant in the cloud forest. Lianas are conspicuous here, but only a meager sampling of orchids (Orchidaceae), ferns and other epiphytes covers the uppermost, exposed limbs. The rather open understory supports a scanty herb layer of ferns and large-leaved perennials such as *Begonia* (Begoniaceae), *Calathea* (Marantaceae), *Costus* (Costaceae), *Dieffenbachia* (Araceae) and *Heliconia* (Heliconiaceae), and these are mostly concentrated in moister spots along streams. The shrub layer contains several species each of Piperaceae (*Piper*), Rubiaceae, and Solanaceae along with numerous tree saplings. Except for the steepest slopes, nearly all of this forest was converted to agriculture and cattle pasture long ago. At Monteverde, this land is used extensively for dairy farming and coffee plantations.

Common canopy species of the Pacific slope wet forest

Species	Family
Beilschmiedia brenesii	Lauraceae
Billia colombiana	Hippocastanaceae
Bourreria costaricensis	Boraginaceae
Cinnamomum cinnamomifolium	Lauraceae
Ficus tuerckheimii	Moraceae
Matayba oppositifolia	Sapindaceae
Persea americana	Lauraceae
Ocotea monteverdensis	Lauraceae
Ocotea whitei	Lauraceae
Pouteria exfoliata	Sapotaceae
Quercus insignis	Fagaceae
Roupala glaberrima	Proteaceae
Sideroxylon stenospermum	Sapotaceae
Styphnolobium monteviridis	Fabaceae/Pap.
Symplocos limoncillo	Symplocaceae

Common shrubs and treelets of the Pacific slope wet forest

Species	Family
Ardisia compressa	Myrsinaceae
Desmopsis bibracteata	Annonaceae
Erythroxylum macrophyllum	Erythroxylaceae
Eugenia monticola	Myrtaceae
Koanophyllon hylonomum	Asteraceae
Meliosma idiopoda	Sabiaceae
Neea psychotrioides	Nyctaginaceae
Piper amalago	Piperaceae
Pisonia silvatica	Nyctaginaceae
Psychotria eurycarpa	Rubiaceae
Psychotria monteverdensis	Rubiaceae
Solanum rovirosanum	Solanaceae
Stauranthus perforatus	Rutaceae
Tabernaemontana longipes	Apocynaceae
Tournefortia glabra	Boraginaceae

Species characteristic of disturbed areas in the Pacific slope wet forest

Species	Family
Acnistus arborescens	Solanaceae
Cecropia obtusifolia	Cecropiaceae
Citharexylum costaricensis	Verbenaceae
Conostegia xalapensis	Melastomataceae
Croton monteverdensis	Euphorbiaceae
Hampea appendiculata	Malvaceae
Inga sierrae	Fabaceae/Mim.
Inga punctata	Fabaceae/Mim.
Myrsine coriacea	Myrsinaceae
Piper auritum	Piperaceae
Psidium guajava	Myrtaceae
Saurauia montana	Actinidiaceae
Solanum umbellatum	Solanaceae
Trema micrantha	Ulmaceae
Viburnum costaricanum	Caprifoliaceae

A somewhat drier vegetation type (Premontane moist forest life zone) occurs below Monteverde in the Río Guacimal and Quebrada Máquina watersheds (Bajo del Tigre) at 900–1200 m. This area appears to be in a rain shadow caused by Cerro Amigos and Cerro Chomogo blocking the trade winds.

Trees characteristic of the premontane moist forest life zone

Species	Family
Annona pruinosa	Annonaceae
Beilschmiedia sp.	Lauraceae
Bursera grandifolia	Burseraceae
Cedrela salvadorensis	Meliaceae
Cosmibuena grandiflora	Rubiaceae
Diospyros sp.	Ebenaceae
Drypetes lateriflora	Euphorbiaceae
Ficus trachelosyce	Moraceae
Maytenus segoviarum	Celastraceae
Montanoa guatemalensis	Asteraceae
Ocotea sinuata	Lauraceae
Ormosia cruenta	Fabaceae/Pap.
Persea caerulea	Lauraceae
Plumeria rubra	Apocynaceae
Sapium macrocarpum	Euphorbiaceae
Ulmus mexicana	Ulmaceae
Viburnum stellatotomentosum	Caprifoliaceae

Cloud forest

On the upper Pacific slope above 1500 m is a dense forest of tall, straight trees with the canopy at 20–35 m (<u>Lower montane wet forest</u> life zone). On the higher peaks and upper Atlantic slope at 1400–1800 m, the cloud forest canopy is lower (15–20 m) and more broken because of its exposure to the strong northeast trade winds and seasonal wind storms (<u>Lower montane rain forest</u> life zone). The elfin forest, found along the windswept ridges of the Brillante Trail on the Continental Divide, and the swamp forest along the Pantanoso Trail in the Preserve belong in this category.

Receiving about 3 m of annual rainfall along with wind-borne mists and cloud cover blown in from the Atlantic side even during the dry season, this forest has a much less seasonal appearance than the moist forest lower down on the Pacific slope. Heavy epiphyte loads and tree bark hidden beneath layers of moss and epiphytes help identify this forest type. The uneven canopy and many treefalls provide sufficient light for a dense understory layer of shrubs and treelets, especially members of the Acanthaceae, Melastomataceae, Piperaceae and Rubiaceae, and large-leaved herbs (*Calathea, Costus, Heliconia, Renealmia*). Numerous species of herbaceous climbers and epiphytes such as aroids (*Anthurium, Monstera, Philodendron*), Cyclanthaceae (*Asplundia*) and bromeliads (*Guzmania, Pitcairnia*) cling to the trunks. On the forest floor, the leaf litter dries out only a few days a year, usually during March and April.

11

Very wet and chilly much of the time, this forest can seem inhospitable; however, on the rare clear days and during the frequent sunny periods around noon, butterflies and bees become active and it can be surprisingly pleasant. Because of its unfavorable climate, as well as the generally steep terrain unsuitable for agriculture, dairying or human habitation, much of the cloud forest still exists.

Common canopy trees of the sheltered Pacific slope cloud forest

Species	Family
Beilschmiedia pendula	Lauraceae
Eugenia guatemalensis	Myrtaceae
Guarea tonduzii	Meliaceae
Inga micheliana	Fabaceae/Mim.
Hasseltia floribunda	Flacourtiaceae
Myrcianthes fragrans	Myrtaceae
Ocotea tonduzii	Lauraceae
Pouteria fossicola	Sapotaceae
Quararibea costaricensis	Bombacaceae
Sapium glandulosum	Euphorbiaceae
Sloanea ampla	Elaeocarpaceae
Symplocos costaricana	Symplocaceae

Common understory trees of the sheltered cloud forest

Species	Family
Ardisia compressa	Myrsinaceae
Casearia tacanensis	Flacourtiaceae
Coussarea austin-smithii	Rubiaceae
Dendropanax querceti	Araliaceae
Koanophyllon pittieri	Asteraceae
Miconia brenesii	Melastomataceae
Palicourea albocaerulea	Rubiaceae
Psychotria jimenezii	Rubiaceae
Psychotria valeriana	Rubiaceae
Tabernaemontana longipes	Apocynaceae
Tovomitopsis psychotriifolia	Clusiaceae

Trees common on exposed ridges and peaks of the cloud forest

Species	Family
Ardisia palmana	Myrsinaceae
Billia hippocastanum	Hippocastanaceae
Brunellia costaricensis	Brunelliaceae
Elaeagia auriculata	Rubiaceae

Ficus crassiuscula	Moraceae
Guarea kunthiana	Meliaceae
Guettarda poasana	Rubiaceae
Hyeronima poasana	Euphorbiaceae
Meliosma vernicosa	Sabiaceae
Ocotea pittieri	Lauraceae
Prestoea acuminata	Arecaceae
Sapium rigidifolium	Euphorbiaceae
Tovomitopsis allenii	Clusiaceae
Weinmannia pinnata	Cunoniaceae

Trees common in disturbed areas of the cloud forest

Species	Family
Bocconia frutescens	Papaveraceae
Clusia spp.	Clusiaceae
Cecropia polyphlebia	Cecropiaceae
Conostegia rufescens	Melastomataceae
Conostegia pittieri	Melastomataceae
Dendropanax sp.	Araliaceae
Gonzalagunia rosea	Rubiaceae
Guettarda poasana	Rubiaceae
Heliocarpus americanus	Tiliaceae
Miconia tonduzii	Melastomataceae
Neomirandea angularis	Asteraceae
Prunus annularis	Rosaceae
Rondeletia monteverdensis	Rubiaceae
Senecio cooperi	Asteraceae
Urera elata	Urticaceae
Viburnum venustum	Caprifoliaceae
Weinmannia wercklei	Cunoniaceae

Atlantic slope rain forest. This forest type (Premontane rain forest life zone) is found on the Atlantic slope between 800 and 1400 m. Receiving 4–8 m of rainfall annually, it is constantly wet and almost aseasonal. The higher ridges intercept the wind-borne clouds and mists even during the dry season, keeping the area socked-in and drizzly. A much taller forest with a canopy at 30–50 m occurs in the sheltered river valleys below 900 m. Fewer epiphytes occur here than in the cloud forest, but it is particularly rich in ferns, aroids, heliconias and other large-leaved herbs. This life zone shares a significant number of species with the cloud forest, but few species reach over as far as the Pacific slope moist forest.

Trees characteristic of rain forest on the Atlantic slope above 1000 m

Species	Family
Alfaroa guanacastensis	Juglandaceae
Allophylus psilospermus	Sapindaceae
Cedrela tonduzii	Meliaceae
Cupania macrophylla	Sapindaceae
Elaeagia uxpanapensis	Rubiaceae
Guarea rhopalocarpa	Meliaceae
Guarea kunthiana	Meliaceae
Guatteria verrucosa	Annonaceae
Hyeronima oblonga	Euphorbiaceae
Inga tonduzii	Fabaceae/Mim.
Meliosma vernicosa	Sabiaceae
Ocotea brenesii	Lauraceae
Ruagea glabra	Sapindaceae
Quararibea costaricensis	Bombacaceae
Trichilia havanensis	Meliaceae

Tree species characteristic of the Atlantic slope rain forest below 1000 m

Species	Family
Alchornea glandulosa	Euphorbiaceae
Cedrela odorata	Meliaceae
Chionanthus oblanceolatus	Oleaceae
Coccoloba tuerckheimii	Polygonaceae
Dussia sp.	Fabaceae/Pap.
Inga barbourii	Fabaceae/Mim.
Iriartea deltoidea	Arecaceae
Mortoniodendron anisophyllum	Tiliaceae
Ocotea dentata	Lauraceae
Oreomunea pterocarpa	Juglandaceae
Sloanea ligulata	Eleaocarpaceae
Pentagonia costaricensis	Rubiaceae
Terminalia bucidoides	Combretaceae
Ticodendron incognitum	Ticodendraceae
Virola sebifera	Myristicaceae

Common trees of disturbed areas in the Atlantic slope rain forest

Species	Family
Cecropia insignis	Cecropiaceae
Hampea appendiculata	Malvaceae
Hedyosmum costaricense	Chloranthaceae
Heliocarpus americanus	Tiliaceae

Inga oerstediana	Fabaceae/Mim.
Miconia smaragdina	Melastomataceae
Myriocarpa longipes	Urticaceae
Perrottetia longistylis	Celastraceae
Piper lanceifolium	Piperaceae
Trema micrantha	Ulmaceae
Urera elata	Urticaceae
Vernonia patens	Asteraceae

PATTERNS OF DISTRIBUTION, ABUNDANCE AND DIVERSITY

Each of these habitats includes a small number of tree species that live only in that type of forest and can be said to be endemic to that zone. The proportion of species in common between two neighboring zones is about 20% of the number of species living in either one. An even smaller number of tree species live in three or more zones and most of these are fast-growing, successional species such as *Hampea appendiculata, Heliocarpus americanus* and *Trema micrantha.* The relatively narrow altitudinal distribution of tree species along with the large number of vegetation zones crowded into a small geographical area result in a surprisingly high tree diversity. We have identified more than 700 tree species from the Monteverde region so far and about 400 of these can be found just in the area between Santa Elena and the Continental Divide. However, the number of species found at any given site is only about 100–150, which is low compared with most lowland wet forests. We identified 114 tree species in a 4-hectare plot of Lower montane wet forest near the MCFP information center (Nadkarni et al. 1995).

We have identified over 3000 plant species from the Monteverde area so far, and we continue to find new ones. More than 870 of these are epiphytes, including 370 species of orchids (Orchidaceae) and 180 species of ferns. Of the total, about 150 species were new to science and most of these are endemic to the Monteverde region.

One often notices that different tree species in the same genus occupy neighboring vegetation zones. The species appear to "turn over" along the altitudinal gradient. Some genera in which this is fairly conspicuous include *Beilschmiedia, Billia, Cedrela, Citharexylum, Conostegia, Meliosma, Quercus, Randia, Sapium, Symplocos,* and *Viburnum.* One needs to realize, though, that the boundaries between life zones are not sharply demarcated and that the tree species do not all stop at the same place along the boundary. Instead, some species extend a bit higher or lower on the slope than others, so that the boundary is blurred. In addition, the higher elevation species often grow lower in the river canyons (presumably because they are limited by dry conditions), and the lower elevation species tend to reach higher elevations along ridges (perhaps because the ridges are sunny and well-drained). In the Monteverde area, however, the altitudinal gradient is steep, and the species ranges can be dramatically narrow.

Some of the familiar species seen in the upper community and lower Preserve at 1400–1550 m, such as *Cedrela tonduzii* and *Guarea rhopalocarpa* (Meliaceae) and *Pouteria fossicola* (Sapotaceae), actually have their main area of distribution on the Atlantic slope. They are simply missing from the high cloud forest, perhaps because this zone is too cold for them. This pattern results in many broken or disjunct species distributions within the Monteverde region. Some species found in the lower Monteverde community (1300–1450 m) wrap around the northern end of the Tilarán mountains to the Atlantic side, as exemplified by *Randia matudae* and *Saurauia montana*. One striking pattern that is difficult to explain are species from the Pacific moist forest, for example *Chionanthus panamensis* and *Ocotea monteverdensis*, that also grow in the tropical wet forest zone on the Atlantic slope down at 400–800 m. Seeds of these species have probably been dispersed over long distances by quetzals, bellbirds, and/or umbrella birds during their seasonal migrations, yet the trees have grown successfully only where climatic conditions are favorable. This pattern of disjunct distributions points to interesting ecological relationships that clearly require further study.

Botanists have found that high tree diversity in tropical forests correlates with high annual rainfall and decreases in progressively drier areas. Lowland forests are generally more diverse than montane forests and areas experiencing seasonal rainfall are generally lower in species numbers than areas that receive a more uniform distribution of annual precipitation. Although plant diversity has been studied little at Monteverde, by inference from patterns in other areas, we would expect to find the highest tree diversity in the tropical wet forest zone on the Atlantic slope and the lowest on the dry Pacific slope, with intermediate numbers in the mountains in between. However, if we look at all plants, not just trees, the large number of epiphytic species concentrated in the cloud forest may make this the habitat of highest plant diversity in the region.

The 20 most important families of trees at Monteverde (above 1200 m) with the number of tree species in each one.

Rubiaceae	37
Lauraceae	36
Melastomataceae	23
Fabaceae	18
Solanaceae	18
Myrtaceae	16
Euphorbiaceae	15
Asteraceae	13
Clusiaceae	11
Moraceae	11
Flacourtiaceae	10
Meliaceae	8

16

Rutaceae	8
Aquifoliaceae	7
Araliaceae	7
Myrsinaceae	7
Celastraceae	6
Sapindaceae	6
Verbenaceae	5
Sapotaceae	4

Chapter 3. Tree Ecology

PHENOLOGY

Phenology refers to the timing and periodicity of natural events in relation to the changes of climate and the seasons. Most tropical trees respond in a predictable way to the seasonality of their environment by flowering and fruiting at specific times of the year and for more or less set periods of time. It is important to know the flowering and fruiting periodicity of plants in order to understand how the plants interact with pollinators, seed dispersers and climate. At Monteverde, several groups of biologists have observed and recorded the times of flowering and fruiting of the plants (see References).

Flowering
At Monteverde, most trees flower just once per year and the time of flowering is predictable. However, different species flower at widely different times, so that in any given month at least 60 species of trees are flowering. During peak months (e.g., March, April, May) over 100 species can be found in flower simultaneously. Minimum flowering activity occurs during September and October—the months of heaviest rainfall, and during November to December—the "windy-misty season."

Fruiting
Fruit production is highest from September through January and lowest from June to August. However, 30–40 species of trees can be found in fruit in any month of the year. Some tree species fruit heavily only at two-year intervals and produce few or no fruits in alternate years. Also, the time of fruiting can shift significantly within the same species depending upon weather conditions (see the El Niño Effect under Climate).

Leaf flushing and leaf drop
New leaf flushing is highest from February to April and lowest from August to December. During the dry season a number of tree species become totally leafless for periods of 1–2 months. Some examples of these deciduous species are *Cedrela tonduzii, Erythrina lanceolata, Meliosma vernicosa, Ormosia cruenta, Persea americana, Sapium glandulosum, Styphnolobium monteviridis,* and *Pouteria fossicola.* These species drop and flush all of their new leaves at once with an annual rhythm. Many other species flush new leaves in association with new twig growth in April and May at or just before the rains begin, while maintaining the old set of leaves. Good examples include many species of Lauraceae and Fabaceae. Most of these species flower at the same time that new leaves and twigs are developing.

POLLINATION

Most of the trees in the Monteverde area are pollinated by insects, and be are by far the most important group of insect pollinators in the area. Moths are easily the second most important pollinator group for trees. Some other insects that contribute to tree pollination are beetles, wasps and butterflies. Only a very few tree species at Monteverde are pollinated by hummingbirds and bats, although these vertebrates can be very important in some lowland forests, and hummingbirds pollinate many species of understory plants and epiphytes in the cloud forest. Finally, wind pollination is also a significant adaptation for pollination on these windy mountain tops.

Most trees have evolved special characteristics for attracting specific pollinators and maximizing the chances for pollination. These adaptations include the size, shape and color of the flowers, whether the flowers open and emit fragrances during the day or night, the volume and chemical make-up of the nectar, and how the anthers are positioned to contact the pollinators. Taken as a whole, these characteristics aid in identification and are useful for understanding how the plants interact with their pollinators.

Bees

We usually divide the bees into large and small bee categories because of notable differences in size and behavior and because they tend to visit different types of flowers. The small bee group is dominated by the stingless bees: *Trigona* and *Melipona* (Apidae), but also includes the sweat bees (Halictidae). Stingless bees do not sting, but instead gouge a wound by biting with their mandibles, or they pull hair. Some species also secrete an irritating chemical into the wound. Stingless bees are social bees that live in large colonies mostly in hollow trees. The nests often have an exit hole in the shape of a tube formed of mud, glue and wood fragments. These bees store honey, and *Melipona* species can be kept in hives like honeybees. They pollinate many species of trees that produce small, white flowers arranged in large inflorescences. These flowers usually produce a strong, sweet honey-like odor and secrete small amounts of nectar. This group of bees and flowers forms the most common pollination system among trees at Monteverde. Some examples include: *Citharexylum* spp., *Hasseltia floribunda*, most species of Myrtaceae, *Prunus* spp., and *Viburnum* spp.

The large bees include *Centris* and *Geischeischia* (Anthophorinae), bumblebees (Apidae: *Bombus*), the larger species of Megachilidae, carpenter bees (*Xylocopa*), orchid bees (Apidae: Euglossinae), and the large, ground-nesting bees at the end of the road in the Preserve and on the tower road (Colletidae: *Crawfordapis luxiana*). These bees primarily visit larger flowers such as the Papilionoid legumes, *Billia colombiana*, and *Styrax* species, as well as the flowers of many lianas, such as Passifloraceae and Apocynaceae. These flowers are often colorful (blue, yellow, purple) and emit pleasant fragrances. Some species produce just a few flowers per day over a long period (the "Trapline"

19

strategy), while others produce a full crown of flowers all at once (the "Big bang" or mass-flowering strategy). The large bees are mostly solitary nesters—each female establishes and provisions a separate nest. Some examples of large bee flowers are *Conostegia* and *Styphnolobium.*

Moths
Most moth-pollinated flowers are small, white, tubular flowers with 5–6-lobed corollas arrayed in large inflorescences. They open in the evening, emit strong fragrances during the night, and secrete nectar as the only pollinator reward. Moth-pollinated trees bloom most abundantly in the wet season, but many species, such as *Cedrela* (Meliaceae) and *Panopsis* (Proteaceae) also flower in the dry season.

Hawk moths or sphinx moths (Sphingidae) constitute an important subgroup of the moths that pollinate many species of trees, shrubs, lianas and epiphytes in our area, as they do throughout the tropics. Hawk moths have long tongues, ranging from 1–25 cm (0.5–10 inches) that they keep coiled like a watch spring beneath their heads. While hovering at flowers, these moths uncoil their tongues and insert them into tubular flowers to extract nectar pooled at the bottom of the floral tube. Hawk moths and their flowers are most abundant during the wet season, especially from May to July when their powerful, gardenia-like fragrances waft through the night air. *Bourreria costaricensis, Guettarda poasana, Inga sierrae,* and *Randia matudae* are examples of hawk moth-pollinated species described in this book.

Other insects
Wasps are involved in a specialized pollination relationship with a small number of trees, but they also visit many of the same species pollinated by *Trigona* bees. Plants specialized for wasp pollination generally have tiny, cup-shaped, white or yellow-green flowers that produce strong honey-like odors. Examples of trees with flowers that attract wasps almost exclusively include *Casimiroa edulis, Maytenus, Sapium, Xylosma,* and *Zanthoxylum.* Figs (*Ficus* spp.) are also pollinated by wasps, but these are tiny, highly specialized wasps of the family Agaonidae, which are derived from parasitic wasps that attack seeds.

Generally considered to be among the most primitive pollinators, the **beetles** are unspecialized for flower feeding. They are mostly nocturnal and are often associated with some of the most ancient angiosperm families such as Annonaceae and Magnoliaceae. The beetles are attracted by odors and feed on specialized nutritive tissues in the flowers. The most common beetle families that include significant pollinators are Curculionidae, Nitidulidae and Scarabaeidae. Examples of beetle-pollinated trees at Monteverde are *Desmopsis bibracteata* and *Guatteria verrucosa* (Annonaceae), and *Magnolia*— and among non-tree groups *Philodendron* and *Xanthosoma* (Araceae), *Asplundia* (Cyclanthaceae), and certain palms (Arecaceae).

A number of trees attract a wide variety of diurnal insects including bees, flies, butterflies, wasps, and beetles and cannot be considered specialized for pollination by a particular group. Examples include the "Güitite" (*Acnistus arborescens*), *Casearia tacanensis, Gonzalagunia rosea*, and many Lauraceae. We think of these trees as being **diurnal generalists**.

Hummingbirds
Although hummingbirds are important pollinators in the Neotropics, very few trees are adapted for pollination by these tiny birds. Because a single tree constitutes a large flowering resource, hummers tend to establish territories on individual trees, favoring self-pollination. The trees that are adapted for hummingbird pollination tend to be small or else they produce relatively small numbers of flowers at one time. *Erythrina lanceolata, Hamelia patens, Malvaviscus palmanus,* and *Symphonia globulifera* are examples of hummingbird-pollinated trees at Monteverde.

However, being very opportunistic, hummingbirds readily find flowers adapted to other pollinator groups—such as bats and hawk moths—to steal nectar whenever possible. Early in the morning, hummers can often be observed visiting flowers that have already been pollinated by nocturnal visitors and they also visit flowers that are just opening at dusk, such as *Inga sierrae* and *Quararibea costaricensis.*

Bats
Bat-pollinated trees are generally more common in the lowlands than in the cloud forest. *Amphitecna haberi* is the only cloud forest tree thought to be pollinated by bats at Monteverde. Several other genera that are typically pollinated by bats in the lowlands are pollinated by hawk moths in the cloud forest, e.g., *Inga* and *Quararibea.* Several bromeliads (*Vriesea*) and other epiphytes (*Capanea grandiflora*–Gesneriaceae, *Markea neurantha*–Solanaceae), and the liana *Mucuna urens* (Fabaceae) have bat-pollinated flowers. On the Pacific slope below Monteverde, *Amphitecna cf. isthmica* (Bignoniaceae), and several Bombacaceae (*Ceiba, Bombacopsis, Quararibea*), are pollinated by bats.

Wind pollination
Several prominent tree groups are wind-pollinated in the cloud forest, for example *Cecropia, Quercus, Ticodendron,* and *Urera* spp. These trees all have unisexual flowers, with the minute male flowers grouped on catkin-like spikes. Tapping a flowering twig on a dry, sunny day will often cause a little pollen cloud to explode into the air.

SEED DISPERSAL AND SEED PREDATION

Seed dispersers
Birds are by far the most important seed dispersers for cloud forest trees. Most bird-dispersed species have either a soft, fleshy, edible fruit or a hard, capsular fruit that opens at maturity to expose several seeds with an edible

covering called an aril. Frequently, the immature fruits are orange or red and then turn black at maturity, offering a contrasting color combination that highlights the location of a fruiting tree. In other cases, such as Lauraceae, the same effect is achieved with a red calyx and black fruit. White and blue fruits are less common, and these are mostly found in the understory. The vast majority of bird fruits fall into two categories:

1) fleshy fruits that range from small, juicy berries containing many, small seeds (*Acnistus, Ficus, Miconia*) to large fleshy fruits with a single, large seed (most Lauraceae) or

2) capsules that are inedible, but which dehisce to expose arillate seeds.

The aril and seed are often contrastingly colored to present a striking visual display, such as a red or white aril partly covering a black seed. Some examples include *Clusia, Cupania, Guarea, Hampea*, and *Tabernaemontana*. Sometimes the inside wall of the fruit valves is also brightly colored (*Sloanea*). In some legumes the pods dehisce to expose contrastingly or brightly colored seeds that have no edible aril, for example *Pithecellobium costaricense* (= *Cojoba costaricensis*) with red pods and black seeds and *Ormosia cruenta* with black pods and scarlet seeds.

Arboreal mammals are also important dispersers for many primary forest trees that form a loose guild. These "mammal fruits" are large, rounded fruits with an edible, fleshy rind (avocado-like) or a tough rind with an edible inner tissue (orange-like). They contain one or few large seeds like an avocado (e.g., *Persea, Pouteria*) or numerous small seeds like a papaya or passion fruit (e.g., *Randia matudae*). At maturity these fruits are usually dull colored, varying from yellow-brown to purplish-green, and they often emit strong, melon-like or unpleasant odors. They also tend to remain on the tree for long periods—often for many months, and do not typically fall when they are ripe. These fruits are thought to be especially adapted for monkeys; however, olingos, kinkajous and coatis are probably also attracted to these species.

Bats. Many of the fruits such as *Cecropia, Conostegia oerstediana*, and *Ficus tuerckheimii* that are favored by bats also attract fruit-eating birds, but other species appear to be eaten almost exclusively by bats (e.g., *Piper amalago, P. auritum, Solanum aphyodendron, S. umbellatum*). Strong odors apparently play an important role in helping bats find these fruits.

Terrestrial mammals. Another set of fruits are protected by an inedible, woody rind or shell. The seeds may have an edible aril like *Inga* spp., or the seed itself may be edible as in *Billia colombiana* and *Panopsis suaveolens*. These fruits may be chewed open on the tree by squirrels, but more commonly agoutis, pacas and other rodents attack them after they fall to the ground.

22

Vertebrate seed eaters

Some of the animals that feed on tree fruits are poor seed dispersers and drop most of the seeds right under the parent tree. Most of these seeds will fail to germinate from lack of adequate light levels or they can be wiped out by fungal diseases or herbivores that concentrate on this clumped resource. Tanagers, which often carefully remove the seeds from the fruit pulp, are a good example (G. Murray, pers. comm.). Other fruit and seed eaters, such as agoutis, pacas, and rats probably destroy more seeds than they disperse. However, when these rodents carry away seeds in their cheek pouches and subsequently lose them, they may function as useful dispersers. Parrots and macaws are also considered to be seed predators. They frequently attack immature fruits and they commonly eat the seeds on the fruiting tree without carrying any of them away. Squirrels eat most of the seeds they encounter, but they also scatter-hoard significant quantities that may later escape predation and germinate.

Seed-eating insects

If you inspect seeds and fruits found on the ground, you may notice that some of them have small holes made by departing insects that have developed inside the seeds. Other seeds may have grub-like insect larvae burrowing inside them. Seed weevils (Curculionidae and Bruchidae) are among the most common seed predators at Monteverde, and frequently inhabit Lauraceae, for example. The larvae of certain moths also commonly attack seeds, but these may also feed on the fruit pulp or rind.

Fig wasps are a highly specialized group of seed parasites. The adult wasps lay eggs in about half of the fig flowers within a developing fruit and these grow into fig wasp larvae that eat the developing seeds. The other half of the flowers are pollinated by the female wasps and these mature into viable seeds.

HERBIVORES

Howler monkeys, sloths and squirrels are the most significant mammalian herbivores of cloud forest trees. Although squirrels feed on fruits, seeds, and the occasional insect or bird nestling, plain leaves are also a staple part of their diet. The authors, Michael Fogden and Dan Wenny (pers. comm.) have also observed black guans eating leaves!

Nevertheless, leaf-eating insects are undoubtedly a much more important factor in herbivory than vertebrates. Virtually every plant that one examines in the forest has some evidence of insect damage. The main groups of leaf-eating insects are caterpillars (the larvae of Lepidoptera); grasshoppers, walking sticks, and katydids (Orthoptera); beetles (Coleoptera), and leaf-cutting ants (Hymenoptera: Formicidae).

PART II. Guide to Cloud Forest Trees

Chapter 4. Techniques for Observing, Collecting, and Identifying Trees

OBSERVING

Binoculars are the most important tool for observing trees, just as they are for watching birds. A portable telescope, such as those used by birders can also be useful. One good place to get a closer look at trees is walking along a forest edge where trees branch out lower to the ground because of the available light. You can also observe remnant and open-grown trees in pastures. Also because these trees get more light, they usually flower and fruit more profusely than in the forest. Watch for fallen flowers and fruits along forest trails, then search the trees overhead to identify their source. One can often find some fallen leaves from the same tree to observe leaf characters in the hand.

COLLECTING

Sometimes one needs to get a small sample of the tree under study, just to see the flowers and leaves up close or for showing to others. One can often knock down a twig or a few leaves by throwing a short section from a dead branch found on the ground (1 foot long by 1 inch in diameter is perfect). A more sophisticated method is to throw a weighted line over a small branch so that the weight drops to the ground on the other side. Then, by pulling down on both ends, one can often snap off a twig. Some trees, for example species of Myrtaceae, may be tough and springy and almost impossible to break, while others (some Lauraceae) snap like a match stick.

To collect fresh, undamaged samples for pressing or for more formal identification, we use an aluminum pole with a clipper head attached at one end. A rope attached to the clipper head pulls a blade that clips the twig. One can fit two or three sections of tubing together, but this can be unwieldy. Some commercially available clipper poles made of telescoping fiberglass tubes are light and strong, but also expensive.

A step beyond the weighted string method is to use a sling shot and monofilament fishing line weighted with a sinker to shoot a line over a high branch. This line can then be used to pull over a strong rope for tugging the branch loose or for pulling up a chain saw blade that can saw through a small branch when you pull alternately on either end of the line. Some forestry supply companies sell such chain and rope systems.

Climbing trees is another way to get samples, but some care is recommended. You can be stung when disturbing the nests of ants or wasps or grab a tree viper, and it is easy to fall when hanging onto rotten lianas. More secure methods have been devised. Using telephone pole spikes is an old standby, but it pokes holes in the bark that can facilitate fungal attack. The

French system of sickle-shaped leg irons works very well for ascending straight trunks. The line over the branch method can also be used to pull up a mountain climber's rope. Rather sophisticated gear including harnesses and jumar ascenders is necessary for safe rope climbing. This is a technical skill that should be learned from an expert.

IDENTIFYING

The very best results at tree identification come from having a leafy twig of the unknown tree in hand, preferably one that also has flowers or fruit. This permits one to examine the leaf characteristics up close, to check for latex and extra-floral nectaries, and to shred a leaf to assess any characteristic odor. A 10–20 power hand lens is very useful for inspecting small stipules, details of anther construction, or looking for glandular hairs and translucent dots. If you forget to take along a hand lens, you can turn your binoculars backwards and hold them close to the leaf.

If you do not have a sample in hand—maybe the tree is leaning out over a 200 m drop-off—then use binoculars to observe whether the leaves are compound or simple, alternate or opposite, and if the leaves are smooth (glabrous) or hairy (pubescent), and have toothed margins. These characters, along with the size and shape of the fruit or color of the flowers, can narrow down the choices quickly and efficiently. In checking for compound leaves, it is good to observe the petiole (leaf stalk) carefully—compound leaves often have an expanded, somewhat bulbous base (pulvinus). Also, simple leaves often have twig buds or inflorescences in their axils, while the leaflets of a compound leaf never do. However, some compound leaves do have a small spike or atrophied leaf at the tip of the rachis that can appear similar to the leaf buds normally located at the tip of a simple-leaved twig. One can usually find a few fallen flowers underneath a flowering tree. Important features to note are flower colors, fragrances, and the number of petals, stamens, and styles.

Although fewer cloud forest trees have distinctive bark or trunk shapes than species in the lowlands (and the bark is mostly covered by epiphytes anyway), we do have a few notable examples here. *Myrcianthes fragrans* (Myrtaceae) has a smooth, peeling bark like the guava, and the bark of *Cedrela* is checkered. *Viburnum, Bourreria, Chionanthus* and *Ilex* have deeply fluted trunks, and all *Sloanea* species have buttresses. In addition, most species of Apocynaceae, Euphorbiaceae, Moraceae, and Sapotaceae have white or beige latex in the bark and twigs. Foresters learn to identify many of the large, commercially-important wood species just by observing bark characteristics such as color, odor, thickness and even taste, and the color and hardness of the underlying wood. Botanists, on the other hand, pay little attention to tree trunks, but want to carefully inspect the leaves, flowers and fruits. If you keep some of these useful characteristics in mind and note them when observing an unknown tree, you can go a long way toward making an identification.

26

RESOURCES

This book serves as only a beginning for the process of identifying a tree. It includes only 88 common and conspicuous species out of about 730 that occur in the Monteverde region. So, obviously, if you travel to the Peñas Blancas or San Luis Valleys or happen to run into a less common species, you may not find it in this book. On the other hand, we mention many related or similar-looking species from the Monteverde area under the Similar species section of each tree description. When you are unable to identify your specimen with this book, you will have to take it to the Instituto Nacional de Biodiversidad or the Museo Nacional de Costa Rica in San José where the National Herbarium is housed. There, dried, pressed samples of most of the species of plants known from the country are kept for study and reference. A library with floras (technical manuals covering the plants of whole countries or geographic regions) can also be used for reference. These books contain keys, descriptions and illustrations that can help to positively identify an elusive specimen. Then you can compare your specimen with those in the collection to see if they closely match. However, the fastest and easiest way to identify a plant is to show it to someone familiar with the flora of the area in question. A number of pertinent references are listed in Appendix 5.

27

Chapter 5. Identification Guide

This identification guide consists of two parts: 1) some simple keys that help to divide the trees into small groups, and 2) species descriptions with illustrations.

The first key, VEGETATIVE KEY TO MAJOR GROUPS (including an illustrated version), is the key for those who have no patience with keys. You can use this key to quickly identify which of the ten major groups fits your plant. Then go to the page indicated for that group and begin paging through the illustrations. The species of each major group are listed in alphabetical order by species name.

A second set of keys, KEYS TO SPECIES WITHIN THE TEN MAJOR GROUPS, uses leaf, flower and fruit characters to divide the species of each of the ten major groups into sets of two to seven species. Each species name is followed by a short description of characters that distinguish that species. Each group has a separate key for specimens with flowers or with fruits. After tentatively identifying your tree by following the keys and character summaries, read the information about that species in the descriptions to determine if it matches your specimen (see sample page at the end of this chapter).

Keep in mind that leaf size, shape, pubescence, development of teeth, and other characters can be highly variable in plants. For example, leaves growing in shade and those on saplings are often much larger than those on flowering twigs. The descriptions used here usually pertain to trees of reproductive age.

SOME DISCLAIMERS AND WARNINGS

1) The keys work for common tree species in Monteverde. In some cases you may not successfully key out a species as there are hundreds not included in this guide.

2) The family boxes scattered through the guide describe local field characters. For example, worldwide, the palm family does not include only "marble-sized fruits," but this is true for our area. The diversity figures given for Monteverde cover the number of species in the region, on both slopes, from the Continental Divide down to 700 m.

3) Occasionally we mention medicinal uses of trees under "comments." In no way are we prescribing the use of these species in curing health problems. For those interested in such uses, we recommend seeking further information from other sources that deal more directly with medicinal properties. With regard to ingesting plants, keep in mind that some tropical species are extremely toxic!

4) Common names vary from region to region (sometimes person to person!); sometimes one name applies to more than one species. We all use common names, however, as they are easy to remember and often descriptive. Scientific names are generally more reliable. We try to give the most up-to-date scientific names in this guide. As scientists classifying tropical plants gather and analyze more information, some names will undoubtedly change. The system of classification for the guide is based on Cronquist (1981). Some taxonomists lump families that we treat separately here. The following are examples:

	May include
Celastraceae	Hippocrateaceae
Urticaceae	Moraceae
Sapindaceae	Hippocastanaceae
Apiaceae	Araliaceae

For more discussion on other classification systems (i.e., Robert F. Thorne, etc.) see Zomlefer, 1994.

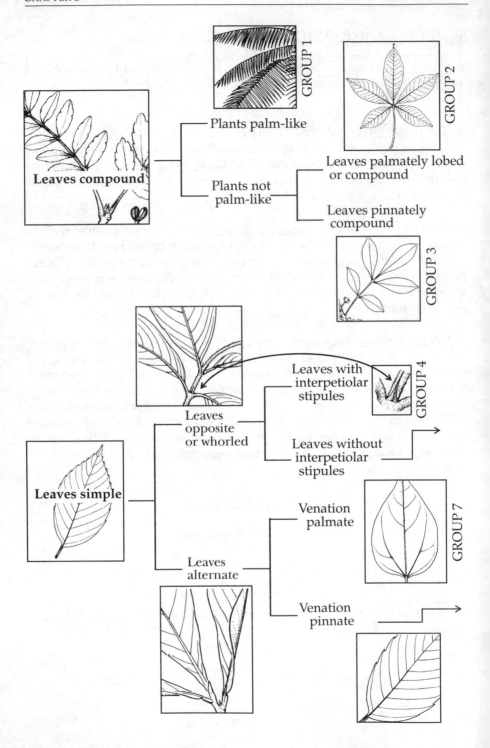

Leaves compound
- Plants palm-like — GROUP 1
- Plants not palm-like
  - Leaves palmately lobed or compound — GROUP 2
  - Leaves pinnately compound — GROUP 3

Leaves simple
- Leaves opposite or whorled
  - Leaves with interpetiolar stipules — GROUP 4
  - Leaves without interpetiolar stipules →
- Leaves alternate
  - Venation palmate — GROUP 7
  - Venation pinnate →

Illustrated Vegetative Key to Major Groups

<u>How to use this key</u>: *While looking at the plant that you want to identify, decide whether its leaves are simple or compound (made up of leaflets). From that point on, you will choose between options in each step of the key—moving from left to right until you end with a numbered GROUP (see next page for locations). Go to that group and flip through the section to match your plant OR use the Group keys on the following pages to progress further.*

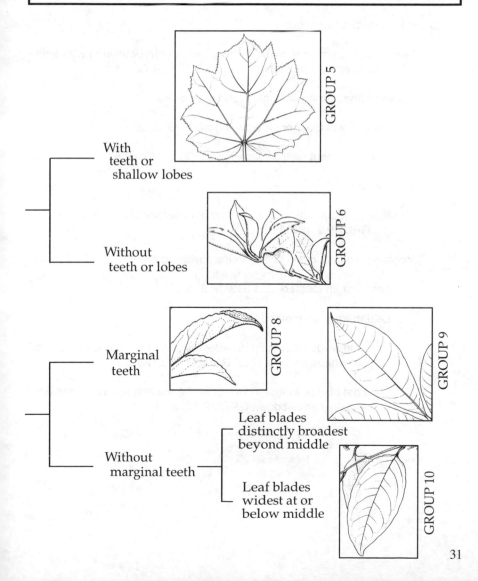

With teeth or shallow lobes — GROUP 5

Without teeth or lobes — GROUP 6

Marginal teeth — GROUP 8

Without marginal teeth

Leaf blades distinctly broadest beyond middle — GROUP 9

Leaf blades widest at or below middle — GROUP 10

31

A. VEGETATIVE KEY TO MAJOR GROUPS

Leaves compound

Plants palm-like ..... GROUP 1, p.44

Plants not palm-like

Leaves palmately compound or palmately lobed ..... GROUP 2, p.50

Leaves pinnately compound ..... GROUP 3, p.58

Leaves simple

Leaves opposite or whorled

Leaves with prominent interpetiolar stipules (intrapetiolar in *Elaeagia*), margin entire (Rubiaceae) ..... GROUP 4, p.72

Leaves without prominent interpetiolar stipules

Leaves with teeth or shallow lobes ..... GROUP 5, p.80

Leaves without teeth or lobes ..... GROUP 6, p.90

Leaves alternate

Venation palmate, with strongly ascending secondary veins at leaf base ..... GROUP 7, p.106

Venation pinnate, basal lateral veins similar to others

Leaf margin toothed ..... GROUP 8, p.116

Leaf margin not toothed

Leaf blades distinctly broadest beyond the middle with a gradually narrowed base ..... GROUP 9, p.128

Leaf blades widest at or below the middle, leaf base and apex equally narrowed ..... GROUP 10, p.144

B. KEYS TO SPECIES WITHIN THE TEN MAJOR GROUPS

GROUP 1. PALMS   p.44

Bactris dianeura (needle-like spines; leaflets rising out of leaf plane; multiple stems; 1.5 cm bright red fruit)

Chamaedorea tepejilote (leaflets of uniform width; yellow stripe on underside of petiole; elliptic gray to black fruit on orange, once-branched infructescence)

Geonoma edulis (leaflets varying in width; inflorescence branched twice; round black fruit on rust-brown branches)

Prestoea acuminata (large multi-stemmed palm with a crownshaft; 1 m inflorescence branched once; 1 cm round black fruit)

GROUP 2. LEAVES PALMATELY COMPOUND OR DEEPLY LOBED   p.50

1. Leaflets 3

Billia colombiana (leaves opposite; no spines; flower white; 4–7 cm round fruit with 3 valves)

Erythrina lanceolata (leaves alternate; spiny trunk; red machete-shaped flowers; beaded pods with red seeds)

1. Leaflets 5 or more

Casimiroa edulis (5 leaflets; small white flowers; 5–8 cm round fleshy fruit with several seeds)

Cecropia obtusifolia (large leaves with 10–12 lobes, not divided to the base; minute flowers and fruits on 10–30 cm pendant spikes)

Oreopanax xalapensis (5–9 leaflets divided to the base; tiny flowers on erect terminal spikes; 1 cm cream to black berries)

GROUP 3. LEAVES PINNATELY COMPOUND   p.58

PLANTS WITH **FLOWERS**

1. Leaflets even numbered (a pair of terminal leaflets)

2. Stamens protruding 1–2 cm beyond corolla

Pithecellobium costaricense (tiny leaflets; 2 cm ball of white flowers)

Inga sierrae (large convex leaflets; nectar glands on rachis; 4 cm brush-like flowers)

2. Stamens about as long as corolla

Cedrela tonduzii (bark checkered; leaf to 1 m; 1 cm cream flowers with 5 petals)

Guarea kunthiana (leaf bud at tip of rachis; 1 cm white flowers with 4 petals)

Zanthoxylum juniperinum (thorns on trunk; translucent dots and citrus odor in leaf; tiny white flowers)

1. Leaflets odd numbered (a single terminal leaflet)

3. Leaflets alternate

Cupania glabra (leaflets toothed; tiny white flowers with 5 petals)

Styphnolobium monteviridis (leaflets without teeth; flowers 2 cm, lavender, shaped like pea flowers)

3. Leaflets opposite

Tapirira mexicana (leaflets without teeth; small cream flowers)

Trichilia havanensis (leaflets entire, rachis ridged, flowers with staminal tube)

Weinmannia pinnata (leaflets toothed, rachis winged; flowers on unbranched spikes)

Zanthoxylum fagara (trunk with thorns; small white 4-parted flowers)

PLANTS WITH **FRUITS (GROUP 3.)**

1. Leaflets even numbered (a pair of terminal leaflets)

2. Fruit an elongate pod

Pithecellobium costaricense (fern-like leaves, twisted cylindrical red pods with elliptic black seeds)

Inga sierrae (large convex leaflets; nectar glands on rachis; flat brown pubescent pods)

2. Fruit a round or oval capsule

Cedrela tonduzii (leaves to 1 m long; bark checkered; 6 cm capsules with 5 valves, seeds winged)

Guarea kunthiana (leaf bud at tip of rachis; capsules to 7 cm with 4 valves, seed with orange aril)

Zanthoxylum juniperinum (thorns on trunk; tiny 2-valved fruit with one black seed)

1. Leaflets odd numbered (a single terminal leaflet)

3. Leaflets alternate

Cupania glabra (toothed leaflets; 2 cm capsules; seed with orange aril)

Styphnolobium monteviridis (no teeth; fruits rubbery beaded pods, often spread along twigs, 1–3 seeds)

3. Leaflets opposite

Tapirira mexicana (leaflets without teeth; 2 cm black drupe; seed coat fibrous)

Trichilia havanensis (leaflets without teeth, rachis ridged, 3-valved fruit capsules with red-arillate seeds)

Weinmannia pinnata (leaflets toothed, rachis winged; tiny pointed capsules with 2 valves)

Zanthoxylum fagara (thorns on trunk; tiny globose, 2-valved capsules)

GROUP 4. LEAVES OPPOSITE, WITH INTERPETIOLAR STIPULES   p.72

PLANTS WITH **FLOWERS**

1. Flowers more than 4 cm long

Cosmibuena valerii (cloud forest above 1500 m; flowers with rounded corolla lobes, red below)

Randia matudae (wet forest below 1500 m; flowers all white with sharp corolla lobes)

1. Flowers less than 4 cm long

Elaeagia auriculata (leaves papery; large intrapetiolar stipules; tiny white flowers; cloud forest)

Gonzalagunia rosea (small pink flowers on long drooping spikes)

Guettarda poasana (fragrant, 2 cm long flowers with 4 lacy petals)

Psychotria elata (2 large red bracts surrounding clusters of white flowers)

Rondeletia monteverdensis (leaves 3 per node; tubular, white flowers with sepals of varying lengths)

PLANTS WITH **FRUITS (GROUP 4.)**

1. Fruit about 1 cm or less

Elaeagia auriculata (large intrapetiolar stipules; fruit a tiny brown capsule)

Gonzalagunia rosea (white spongy fruit; pubescent leaves)

Guettarda poasana (1 cm purple-black fruit)

Psychotria elata (fruit blue-black, grouped between 2 large red bracts; leaf veins ridged on upper surface)

Rondeletia monteverdensis (3 leaves per node, tiny fruit capsules with minute seeds)

1. Fruit 4–8 cm long

Cosmibuena valerii (cylindrical capsules to 8 cm with winged seeds; large rounded stipules)

Randia matudae (fruit smooth green balls to 7 cm with many seeds, small triangular stipules)

GROUP 5. OPPOSITE LEAVES WITH TEETH OR LOBES p.80

PLANTS WITH **FLOWERS**

Conostegia oerstediana (netted venation; 2 cm flowers with 24 orange anthers)

Conostegia xalapensis (leaves beige below, netted venation; flowers white with yellow anthers)

Koanophyllon pittieri (leaves lance-shaped; 5 mm brush-like flowers)

Montanoa guatemalensis (leaves broad with few large teeth; 5 cm white and yellow daisy-like flower heads)

Neomirandea angularis (leaves with large teeth and lobes; flowers lavender; forest edge)

Siparuna tonduziana (leaves hairy with pungent odor; tiny yellow to orange flowers without petals)

PLANTS WITH **FRUITS (GROUP 5.)**

Conostegia oerstediana (leaves with netted venation; fruit blue-black; many tiny seeds)

Conostegia xalapensis (leaves beige below, netted venation; fruits round and black, 8 mm)

Koanophyllon pittieri (leaves lance-shaped; fruits in 5 mm heads, seeds with a hairy wing)

Montanoa guatemalensis (leaves broad with few large teeth; fruiting heads 1–2 cm, seed not winged)

Neomirandea angularis (leaves with large teeth and lobes; seeds winged; second growth)

Siparuna tonduziana (leaves hairy; fruit red warty, teardrop-shaped, with pungent odor)

GROUP 6. OPPOSITE LEAVES, WITHOUT TEETH OR LOBES p.90

PLANTS WITH **FLOWERS**

1. Flowers colored

Bunchosia macrophylla (leaves pubescent; flowers with 5 yellow petals)

Salacia petenensis (tiny red or green flowers on much-branched inflorescences along branches)

Symphonia globulifera (latex yellow; buds pink-red; flowers pink and white like peppermint candy)

1. Flowers white or cream

2. Stamens more than 20

Clusia stenophylla (leaves rubbery; yellow latex; 2 cm white flowers with 6–7 petals)

Eugenia guatemalensis (leaf with translucent dots, weak odor; brush-like flowers with 4 petals)

Myrcianthes fragrans (leaf with translucent dots, aromatic odor; flaking bark; brush-like flowers)

2. Stamens less than 10

Citharexylum costaricensis (small white 5-lobed flowers on pendant spikes)

Viburnum costaricanum (leaves 3 per node; 5-parted flowers on terminal branched inflorescences)

Chionanthus panamensis (trunk channeled; flowers with 4 narrow petals)

Pisonia sylvatica (short spines on twigs; flowers forming a pendant ball)

Tabernaemontana longipes (white latex; flowers with 5 brown-tipped petals)

PLANTS WITH **FRUITS (GROUP 6.)**

1. Fruit about 1 cm, mostly round, fleshy berries

Citharexylum costaricensis (fruit orange to brown to black on pendant spikes; 1 seed)

Myrcianthes fragrans (fruit red or black; 1 seed; translucent dots in leaves)

Pisonia sylvatica (1 cm dry fruit with angular ribs and sticky glands on surface)

Viburnum costaricanum (round black fruit in erect umbels; 1 seed; leaves 3 per node)

1. Fruit 2–7 cm long, of various shapes

2. Leaves commonly more than 15 cm long

Bunchosia macrophylla (leaves pubescent; fruit orange, round, and smooth)

Clusia stenophylla (leaves thick and fleshy; yellow latex; fruit a yellow-green, capsule with arillate seeds)

2. Leaves rarely more than 15 cm long

Chionanthus panamensis (yellow drupe with grooved seed; narrow, glabrous leaf)

Eugenia guatemalensis (brown to yellow drupe; leaf with blunt tip and translucent dots)

Salacia petenensis (7 cm leathery brown ball containing 3–6 large elongate seeds)

Symphonia globulifera (yellow latex; 2.5 cm elliptic green fruit with one seed)

Tabernaemontana longipes (white latex; paired dangling capsules containing many seeds with red-orange arils)

GROUP 7. LEAVES ALTERNATE AND VENATION PALMATE   p.106

PLANTS WITH **FLOWERS**

1. Leaves toothed or lobed

Croton monteverdensis (old leaves turn orange before falling; small green-white flowers; 2 nectar glands at petiole tip)

Hasseltia floribunda (2 nectar glands at leaf base; small white flowers with 30-40 stamens)

Heliocarpus americanus (large, rounded leaves; flowers yellow-green with 4 narrow petals)

Malvaviscus palmanus (conspicuous stipules; large red flowers with 5 twisted petals forming a tube)

Trema micrantha (small, narrow, toothed leaves; tiny white flowers along leafy twigs)

Urera elata (large, oval, toothed leaves; clusters of tiny green or pink flowers without petals)

1. Leaves without teeth or lobes

Hampea appendiculata (leaves rusty/beige below; 1.5 cm yellow flowers)

Piper auritum (large heart-shaped leaves with sassafras odor; erect 20 cm flower spikes)

PLANTS WITH **FRUITS (GROUP 7.)**

1. Fruit a round juicy berry

Hasseltia floribunda (paired glands at leaf base, 1 cm red-purple berry)

Malvaviscus palmanus (red 5-lobed fruit; conspicuous stipules)

Trema micrantha (tiny orange fruit; short petioles; small, narrow toothed leaves, in a plane)

Urera elata (tiny red-orange fruit; large, oval toothed leaves with long petioles)

1. Fruit not a round juicy berry

Croton monteverdensis (old leaves turn orange before falling; fruit a round, exploding capsule)

Hampea appendiculata (leaves rusty beige below; fruit a 3-lobed capsule, seed black, with white aril)

Heliocarpus americanus (small ear-like lobes at leaf base; fruit flat with red hairy soft spines)

Piper auritum (leaf heart-shaped; a long pendant fruiting spike with minute seeds)

GROUP 8. LEAVES ALTERNATE, TOOTHED AND VENATION PINNATE p.116

PLANTS WITH **FLOWERS**

1. Flowers with typical showy petals

Casearia tacanensis (leaves in a plane, yellow-green flowers with 5 petals)

Clethra lanata (oval, pubescent leaves, small white flowers in spikes)

Meliosma idiopoda (narrow glabrous leaves with sparse teeth, tiny white flowers on distal spikes)

Saurauia montana (leaves saw-toothed, to 30 cm long; 2 cm white flowers with 5 petals, many orange stamens)

Symplocos limoncillo (flowers white shaded with pink; over 40 stamens forming a tube)

1. Flowers without typical showy petals

Bocconia frutescens (leaves deeply lobed; watery orange sap; gray-green flowers on large branched inflorescences)

Sapium glandulosum (white latex, tiny red-green flowers on erect spikes)

Ticodendron incognitum (leaves toothed, male flowers in catkins; female flowers in leaf axils with forked style)

PLANTS WITH **FRUITS (GROUP 8.)**

1. Fruit dehiscent

Bocconia frutescens (deeply lobed leaf; small, 2-valved capsules; one seed with red aril)

Clethra lanata (pubescent leaf; 3-valved capsules with minute winged seeds)

Sapium glandulosum (3-lobed capsules; 3 black seeds with red arils)

Saurauia montana (leaf 15–30 cm, saw-toothed; hairy 2 cm fruit with 5 valves; many tiny seeds in a gelatinous pulp)

1. Fruit fleshy, indehiscent

Casearia tacanensis (fleshy 3–5 cm indehiscent capsules, many seeds with juicy orange arils)

Meliosma idiopoda (narrow leaf with few teeth; 1 cm cream fruit; 1 seed with faceted surface)

Symplocos limoncillo (fruit blue-gray with violet inner flesh; scar at tip)

Ticodendron incognitum (almond-shaped green drupe; grooved seed)

GROUP 9. LEAVES OBOVATE, DISTINCTLY WIDEST BEYOND MIDDLE p.128

PLANTS WITH **FLOWERS**

1. Leaves mostly more than 20 cm long

Amphitecna haberi (leaves spiraled; large green-white flowers in leaf axils)

Cordia cymosa (large oval leaf; small white flowers in flat-topped inflorescences)

Meliosma vernicosa (swollen petiole base, tiny white flowers in large inflorescences)

Pouteria fossicola (white latex; 1 cm tubular cream flowers along twig)

Quararibea costaricensis (leaves in a plane, 3 cm white flowers in leaf axils)

Sloanea ampla (buttressed; 1 cm cream flowers with many brush-like stamens)

1. Leaves rarely reaching 20 cm long

Beilschmiedia pendula (flowers yellow with 6 tepals; leaves elliptic; bark reddish)

Daphnopsis americana (4 petals and stamens; elastic fibers in leaf)

Ocotea tonduzii (flowers with 6 yellow tepals, 9 stamens; leaves obovate with 1 cm petiole)

Panopsis suaveolens (white flowers on spikes, 4 recurved petals)

Persea americana (flowers yellow-green; leaves with 2–3 cm petiole)

Quercus corrugata (gnarly, buttressed trunk; tiny green flowers in catkins)

Sideroxylon stenospermum (white latex; small white 5-lobed flowers)

PLANTS WITH **FRUITS (GROUP 9.)**

1. Fruit large (more than 3 cm long)

Amphitecna haberi (13 cm pendant fruit, oblong with pointed tip; many seeds)

Beilschmiedia pendula (black drupe without cupule)

Panopsis suaveolens (5 cm lemon-shaped fruit with hard shell; 1 seed)

Persea americana (round avocado fruit with one large seed)

Pouteria fossicola (elliptic, warty green-brown fruit 7 to 12 cm; 1–2 smooth elliptic seeds)

Quercus corrugata (sucker leaves toothed; fruit a large acorn)

Sloanea ampla (fruit red with long woody spines)

1. Fruit small (3 cm long or less)

Cordia cymosa (large oval leaf; 1 cm white berries)

Daphnopsis americana (round, white fruit; bark and leaf tissue stringy)

Meliosma vernicosa (2 cm brown, round fruit; seed faceted)

Ocotea tonduzii (fruit green to black with red cupule)

Quararibea costaricensis (elliptic yellow fruit with 1 seed)

Sideroxylon stenospermum (black, round fruit with 1 globose seed)

GROUP 10. LEAF BLADES BROADEST AT OR BELOW MIDDLE   **p.144**

PLANTS WITH **FLOWERS**

1. Flowers white or cream

  2. Flowers over 3 cm long

      Bourreria costaricensis (leaf oval, no teeth; 4 cm tubular flower with 5 lobes)

      Magnolia poasana (10 cm broad flower with 6 free petals; large deciduous stipules)

  2. Flowers 1 cm long or less

    3. Flowers with 5 petals

      4. Stamens 5

        Acnistus arborescens (flowers grouped in axils of large soft leaves, anthers cream)

        Ardisia compressa (5 yellow anthers, recurved petals; pellucid streaks in leaf)

        Ardisia palmana (as above, but large 15–30 cm leaves held in a plane)

        Solanum aphyodendron (1 cm flowers with 5 yellow anthers; strong unpleasant odor in leaves)

      4. Stamens 10 or more

        Erythroxylum macrophyllum (10 stamens; persistent, papery stipules)

        Prunus annularis (15–20 stamens; bitter almond odor in twigs)

41

3. Flowers with 4 petals

Stauranthus perforatus (4 petals and stamens; double pulvinus; pellucid dots)

1. Flowers green, yellow, or pink

5. Flowers with a corolla or petals

6. Flowers 2-3 cm long

Cestrum sp. (narrow tubular green to purple 2 cm flowers with 5 lobes)

Guatteria verrucosa (6 broad yellow petals; anthers coalesced in a central disk)

6. Flowers less than 1 cm long

Beilschmiedia pendula (see Group 9)

Myrsine coriacea (tiny green 5-parted flowers grouped along twigs; red translucent dots; secondary veins obscure)

Ocotea whitei (6 yellow-orange tepals, 9 stamens; leaf tips long and twisted)

5. Flowers without showy petals, hidden inside a fruit-like globe

Ficus tuerckheimii (white latex; short stipules; leaves oval)

Ficus crassiuscula (white latex; long stipules; leaves elliptic)

PLANTS WITH **FRUITS (GROUP 10.)**

1. Fruit more than 3 cm long

2. Fruit nearly round

Bourreria costaricensis (leaves oval; purple fruit 4-seeded)

Ficus crassiuscula (white latex; fruit yellow-green, surface warty; tiny seeds)

2. Fruit distinctly longer than wide

Beilschmiedia pendula (see Group 9)

Magnolia poasana (dehiscent cone-like fruit; red arillate seeds)

Ocotea whitei (black drupe with red cupule)

1. Fruit 1-2 cm long

Ficus tuerckheimii (fruit red with many seeds)

Guatteria verrucosa (round, black fruit in clusters)

Prunus annularis (fruit black, almond odor in twigs)

Solanum aphyodendron (1.5 cm yellow-green fruit, many flat seeds; rank odor)

Stauranthus perforatus (leaf with double pulvinus, translucent dots;

42

olive-like black fruit)

1. Fruit 1 cm or less

3. Fruit one-seeded

Ardisia compressa (fruit black; leaves fleshy; translucent dots and streaks)

Ardisia palmana (as above, but leaves 15–30 cm, held in a plane)

Erythroxylum macrophyllum (fruit elliptic, from yellow to red)

Myrsine coriacea (tiny black fruits in dense clusters along twigs)

3. Fruit with several to many seeds

Acnistus arborescens (7 mm orange berries with many tiny flat seeds)

Cestrum sp. (fruit purple-black with 1–12 elliptic to angular seeds)

EXAMPLE OF PAGES IN MAIN BODY OF IDENTIFICATION GUIDE

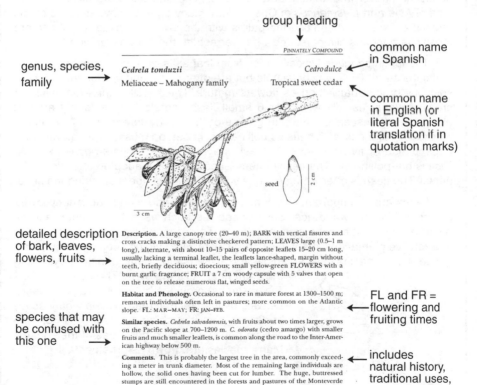

59

GROUP 1.

PALMS

ARECACEAE (PALMAE)—Palm family

Field characters: *palm–like aspect, stem nodes with prominent leaf scars forming rings around stem, compound leaves with pleated venation, one-seeded marble-sized fruits.*

Palms are usually easy to recognize by their large compound leaves with long, strong leaf stalks (petioles) and numerous parallel secondary veins. The leaves are of three types: palmately compound, pinnate with usually numerous leaflets (pinnae in palms) angling away from a strong central rachis, or with the pinnae undivided except at the tip and therefore appearing entire with a forked apex. The stems often have very conspicuous nodes where fallen leaves have left a scar, and stilt roots are typical of certain species. Some species have almost no above ground stem or a very short one and a few are climbers (Rattans of Asia and *Desmoncus* of Costa Rica). Many species have multiple stems (colonial). One could confuse the palms with the Cyclanthaceae, but these are mostly herbaceous climbers, and when terrestrial, they are never woody.

The inflorescences typically arise from leaf axils or from the leafless nodes along the stem. They may be simple but are often large and branched, with conspicuous bracts that fall off as flowers mature. The sessile, unisexual white or cream flowers, usually with 3 or 6 small fleshy petals, are uniformly arrayed along the inflorescences, often in groups of three. The flowers can have either pleasant fragrances, with bees as pollinators, or can be musky or fetid, with, perhaps, beetle or fly pollinators. At least one species of *Calypterogyne* in Costa Rica is bat-pollinated. The fleshy one-seeded fruits, are adapted for animal dispersal. The flesh is often stringy and oily with a layer of fibers covering the seed.

Palms are an important component of the understory and subcanopy layers of tropical forests worldwide. Several species such as date, coconut, and oil palms are of great commercial importance. The African oil palm (*Elaeis*), grown in extensive plantations in southwestern Costa Rica, yields cooking oil and margarine. Many species have an edible apical meristem, "heart of palm"; extracting

the palm heart kills the stem. The pejibaye (*Bactris gasipaes*) provides both fruit and palm heart. Leaves of the "palma real" (*Attalea butyracea*) serve as roof thatching for "ranchos" on the Nicoya peninsula and other areas of the country. Many species are grown as ornamentals.

fruits of Pejibaye (*Bactris gasipaes*)

Species Diversity—World: 2650; **Costa Rica:** 96; **Monteverde:** 30

See next five pages for local examples of **Arecaceae.**

Bactris dianeura

Arecaceae – Palm family

Huiscoyol

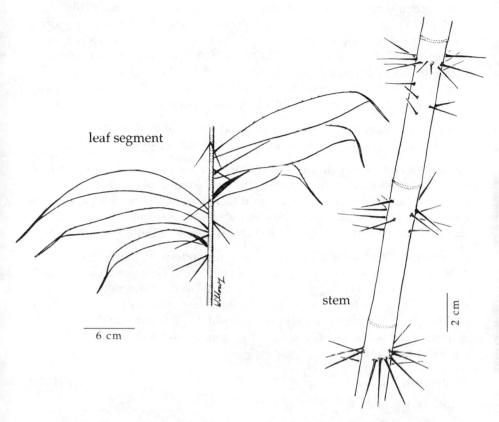

leaf segment

stem

6 cm

2 cm

Description. A treelet (3–8 m, 2–3 cm in diameter), usually growing in multi-stemmed clumps; stems and leaves with needle-like black spines; LEAVES 1.5–2 m, with about 30 leaflets in alternating groups of 2–4 and not all in the same plane; small white FLOWERS in 15–20 cm INFLORESCENCES, the spathe spiny and persisting in flower; FRUIT almost round, bright red-orange; one hard black seed with 3 holes near one end.

Habitat and Phenology. Occasional in old light gaps of primary forest, more common in older secondary forest at 1200–1500 m. FL: APR–MAY; FR: MAY.

Similar species. *Bactris* is the only local palm with leaflets not held in the plane of the midvein. Another spiny species *Bactris hondurensis*, grows in the Peñas Blancas valley below 1000 m. *Bactris gasipaes* (pejibaye) is cultivated.

Comments. The fruit and stone-hard seeds are larger than those of the other palms included here. It is unpleasant to grasp the stem of this palm when sliding downhill out of control.

45

Chamaedorea tepejilote *Pacaya de danta*
Arecaceae – Palm family

Description. An understory treelet (2–7 m, 4–7 cm diameter), the solitary trunk green with internodes about 5 cm long, stem often with stilt roots; LEAVES 1–1.5 m long, a yellow stripe along underside of rachis and petiole, about 20 pairs of leaflets (pinnae) of uniform width, conspicuously narrowed at base and slightly S-shaped; INFLORESCENCE in bud with long-pointed spathe held nearly vertical; dioecious; small cream FLOWERS on a pale yellow, once-branched inflorescence up to 65 cm long; FRUIT elliptic, to 13 mm long, gray-green (immature) to black (mature) on red-orange branches.

Habitat and Phenology. Common in cloud forest understory above 1500 m; also common in Peñas Blancas. FL: JUN–AUG; FR: FEB–MAY.

Similar species. Easily distinguished from *Geonoma edulis*, which has brown stems and pinnae of varying widths; the combination of stilt roots, a yellow stripe on the petiole, many pinnae, and lack of multiple stems separates this from any other *Chamaedorea* in the area. *Prestoea acuminata* also has even pinnae but is much larger, has a crown shaft, and lacks adventitious stilt roots.

Comments. This is one of the most common understory palms occurring at 1450–1500 m on both slopes. Above this elevation, *Geonoma edulis* is usually more abundant. The two species overlap in the wetter forests on the Atlantic slope. Tasting the fruits of this species may burn your mouth like hot jalapeño peppers. Eating the palm heart (the soft, edible meristem tissue) causes an unpleasant sensation of hunger in the stomach that can be relieved by eating something sweet.

Geonoma edulis *Súrtuba*
Arecaceae – Palm family

Description. An understory treelet (2–5 m), solitary tan stem, leaf scars crowded at top of stem; LEAVES about 2 m long, with pinnae of varying widths, the base broad (about as wide as the middle); INFLORESCENCES on stem just below the leaves, branched twice with numerous small pinkish-white or beige FLOWERS; FRUIT 7 mm, nearly round, olive-green when immature, black when mature.

Habitat and Phenology. Common in forest understory and disturbed sites in cloud forest above 1500 m. FL: sporadic, almost any month; FR: irregular and not synchronized.

Similar species. *Chamaedorea tepejilote* is a solitary palm of similar size with pinnae of uniform width, a yellow stripe on the underside of the rachis, and longer internodes. *G. edulis* is also the only tall palm in the area with twice-branched inflorescences.

Comments. This is the most abundant palm in the 3–5 m treelet layer of the upper elevation cloud forest.

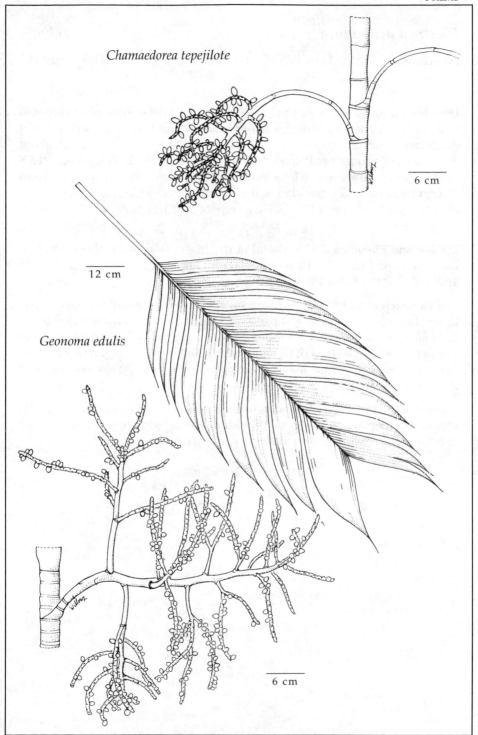

Chamaedorea tepejilote

6 cm

12 cm

Geonoma edulis

6 cm

Prestoea acuminata

Palmito

Arecaceae – Palm family

"Palm heart"

Description. A tall subcanopy palm (5–15 m), with either solitary or clustered stems to 10 cm diameter, brown, with internodes about 10 cm long, a prominent green crownshaft about 75 cm at top of stem; LEAVES 2–2.5 m long with about 25–35 pairs of pinnae evenly spaced and of uniform width; INFLORESCENCES attached below leaves, to 1 m long, protected by a heavy, canoe-shaped spathe to 115 cm long, rachillae (branches of the inflorescence) white, unbranched, 45–60 cm long; small white FLOWERS in groups of 3; FRUIT globose, 12 mm, black when mature.

Habitat and Phenology. Occasional in the high cloud forest above 1550 m; most common along the Pantanoso Trail, a few along the Río and Nuboso Trails, also in the Santa Elena Reserve. FL: JUN–JUL; FR: ?

Similar species. *Prestoea longepetiolata,* at slightly lower elevations, has similar leaves, but it has persistent leaf bases and the stem ranges from only 0.5–1.5 m. *Chamaedorea tepejilote* has a more slender stem with stilt roots at the base. *Geonoma edulis* has leaflets of varying width. Three other tall palms with similar leaves occur in Peñas Blancas: *Euterpe macrospadix, Chamaedorea* sp., and *Prestoea decurrens.*

Comments. This species has been used locally as a source of "palmito," the soft, edible meristem found inside the stem apex. Extracting the palm heart kills the stem. Parrots eat the fruits in some areas.

6 cm

young
crownshaft

GROUP 2.
LEAVES PALMATELY COMPOUND
OR PALMATELY LOBED

Billia colombiana
Hippocastanaceae – Horse-chestnut family

Cucaracho
"Cockroach"

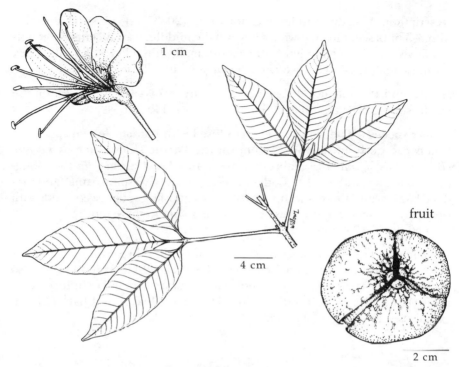

fruit

Description. A large canopy tree (15–35 m); BARK chipped and scalloped; LEAVES opposite with 3 leaflets, without teeth; large bilaterally symmetric FLOWERS with 4–5 white petals flushed with yellow at base; FRUIT a 4–7 cm brown capsule with husk splitting into 3 valves (red inside); containing 1 round red-brown seed.

Habitat and Phenology. Common in the drier forest below the Preserve (1200–1450 m), and also on the Atlantic side. FL: FEB–JUN; FR: SEP–NOV.

Similar species. *Billia hippocastanum* is similar, but has scarlet flowers and occurs in the high cloud forest above 1550 m (Chomogo and Pantanoso Trails, and in Santa Elena Reserve).

Comments. The flowers are fragrant and attract large bees. Old flowers turn red and accumulate on the ground under flowering trees. The fruit seems to lack any kind of attraction or reward for dispersal by animals other than for rodents, such as porcupines, which eat the seeds. The name apparently derives from the many insects (such as cockroaches) that hide under the loose bark chips on the trunk during the dry season. *Billia* wood is hard, with pink and red marbling. It is used for construction and firewood.

51

Casimiroa edulis *Matasano*

Rutaceae – Rue and Citrus family

Description. A medium to large canopy tree (20–35 m); LEAVES alternate with 3–5 pubescent leaflets widest beyond the middle, translucent yellow dots (easily visible with a hand lens); dioecious; small white FLOWERS with 4 petals and stamens; FRUIT a 5–8 cm ball with an edible fleshy rind.

Habitat and Phenology. Occasional in mature, moist and wet forest on the Pacific slope from 900–1500 m. FL: FEB, JUL–SEP; FR: AUG–SEP.

Similar species. The leaves can be confused with palmate-leaved species of Bombacaceae found below 1100 m on the Pacific slope, such as *Pachira (Bombacopsis) quinata* (5 glabrous leaves) and *Ceiba aesculifolia* (5–8 long-pointed leaflets with teeth). Both of these species have spiny trunks and produce large, white flowers with many stamens and large, dehiscent pods with wool-covered seeds. The leaves of *Oreopanax xalapensis* have more leaflets and the petioles are 2–3 times longer.

Comments. The small, unisexual flowers are visited by wasps and stingless bees. The trees are sometimes cultivated for their edible fruit, but they also occur as native trees in primary forest. The fruits are reputed to induce sleepiness (Holdridge and Poveda 1975). The seeds, leaves and bark contain casimirose, a toxic glucoside, which can be fatal in large doses.

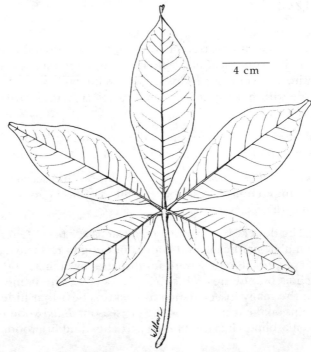

4 cm

52

Cecropia obtusifolia
Cecropiaceae – Cecropia family

Guarumo

Cecropia

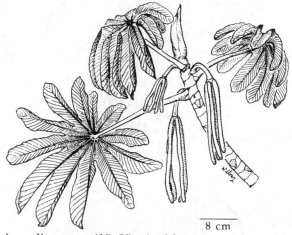

8 cm

Description. A medium tree (15–25 m) with very open branching pattern like a candelabra and conspicuous segmented internodes on the branches and smaller stems, often with stilt roots; LEAVES bunched at twig tips, 0.5–1 m across, with long petioles and about 10–12 lobes separated 3/4 of the way to the base, about 30 pairs of lateral veins on the largest lobes, upper surface scratchy; dioecious; minute FLOWERS on cream-yellow pendant, finger-like spikes to 35 cm long and 10 mm diameter ($\male$ inflorescences shorter and more slender); FRUIT similar to flowers but spikes thicker, about 1.5 x 15–35 cm.

Habitat and Phenology. Common in light gaps, forest edges and pastures at 900–1450 m. FL: all year (pcak in MAR–MAY); FR: APR–JUN, JUL–SEP, DEC.

Similar species. *Cecropia polyphlebia*, which grows at 1500–1800 m on the Pacific side, has shorter inflorescences (to 10 cm long) and about 40 pairs of lateral veins on the largest leaf lobes. *Cecropia insignis*, common on the Atlantic slope, has smooth upper leaf surfaces with about 20 pairs of veins.

Comments. This is one of the most distinctive species in the area. At night, the dead leaves on the ground look like curled-up armadillos. The fallen hairy, red bracts are also distinctive. The flowers are wind-pollinated. The fruits are eaten by many species of birds and mammals, including fruit bats. Many species of *Cecropia* harbor vicious stinging ants of the genus *Azteca*. The ants, which nest in the hollow nodes of the stems and branches, aggressively guard the plant from potential herbivores such as caterpillars and grasshoppers. The tree provides glycogen-rich Müllerian bodies on the petioles for the ants. The lower elevation species (*insignis, obtusifolia,* and *peltata*) nearly always have ant colonies, but the higher elevation *polyphlebia* rarely does. In the past, large stems were split and used as water troughs, gutters, etc.

53

Erythrina lanceolata

Fabaceae – Legume family

(Papilionoideae – Pea and Bean subfamily)

Poró

Machete flower

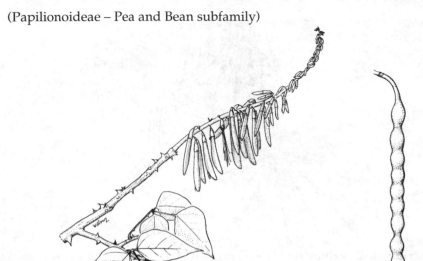

4 cm

Description. A small tree (4–8 m); TRUNK and branches with stout, recurved spines; LEAVES alternate with 3 leaflets, often with spines on the petiole and rachis; large sword–shaped, scarlet FLOWERS in clusters near the tip of often leafless twigs; FRUIT an elongate cylindrical pod with a pointed tip dehiscing to expose hard bright red seeds without an aril.

Habitat and Phenology. Occasionally seen in old light gaps in wet forest at 900–1300 m, but more common in secondary forest and edges. FL: FEB–MAR, NOV; FR: MAY–JUN.

Similar species. This is the only *Erythrina* in our area, but another species, *gibbosa* (with a bulbous flower base), grows below 1300 m on the Atlantic slope. *E. berteroana* (with similar, but paler orange flowers) can be seen along the lower end of the road to the Inter-American highway.

Comments. This tree is sometimes planted as a living fence post in the Monteverde area. One makes a "living fence post" by sticking a branch segment in the ground. Successful stakes will root and produce new trees, thus providing living posts that can endure for many years, while at the same time being a source for future posts. Two other species with bright orange flowers (December to February) are used commonly as shade trees over coffee plantations in the Central Valley between San Ramon and San José.

54

FABACEAE (LEGUMINOSAE)—Legume family

Field characters: *alternate compound leaves with swollen petiole bases and cylindrical leaflet stalks, a green bean odor in shredded leaves, and fruit often a two-sided pod with bean-like seeds.*

The Fabaceae is one of the largest plant families and also one of the most vegetatively diverse including herbs, shrubs, vines, lianas, and trees, but very few epiphytes. Most species have pinnately or bipinnately compound leaves and woody stems. The tree species at Monteverde belong to two of the three subfamilies. The Mimosoideae (mimosa group) have flowers with a reduced and inconspicuous tubular calyx and corolla with radial symmetry, numerous conspicuous stamens forming a brush-like mass, and a long straight style. The Papilionoideae (pea flower group) have bilaterally symmetric flowers with 5 petals including a broad showy petal with a different shape from the others, 9 stamens concealed between the petals, and a short elbowed style. The subfamily Caesalpinoideae (Cassia group) is common in the lowlands, but does not reach Monteverde. The flowers are similar to those of the Papilionoideae, but they have 10 stamens, and there is little specialization in the shape of the petals.

One can recognize legumes by the characteristics given above as well as stipules, and the presence, in some species, of extrafloral nectar glands on the rachis. The distinctive flowers could only be confused with some species of Polygalaceae, which have simple leaves. The fruit is usually a tough pod with several seeds (some species have sweet arils), but a few are drupes. Most bean seeds have a hard shell and are capable of undergoing a dormant period, but those like *Inga*, with a soft-skin, must germinate quickly.

Legumes occur throughout the world in almost all habitats. They are among the most diverse and abundant trees and lianas in both lowland dry forests and rain forests, but less dominant at higher elevations. Bees pollinate most species of Papilionoideae, although a few, like *Mucuna*, are bat-pollinated, and *Erythrina* provides nectar for hummingbirds. Mass-flowering trees in the Costa Rican dry forest support a large number of solitary bees. The mimosoids attract a number of different pollinator groups including moths and bats that go to those species producing nectar and fragrance at night, and hummingbirds, that visit bright red flowers of *Calliandra*. Bees and butterflies are the main pollinators of caesalpinoid legumes. Seed dispersal agents include birds and mammals, wind, water, and explosive dehiscence. The leaves of many legumes fold up at night and those of the sensitive plant (*Mimosa pudica*) also drop down at a touch to disappear from herbivores. Ant acacias, of the more seasonal habitats of Costa Rica, have a mutualistic relationship with aggressive stinging ants (*Pseudomyrmex*) that protect the leaves from herbivores. The ox eye, sea heart and nicker nut seeds that float up onto beaches come from legume vines and shrubs.

This family includes important food plants such as beans, peanuts, peas, and lentils as well as forage crops (alfalfa and clover), and flowering ornamentals— wisteria, cassia, coral bean (*Erythrina*). The root nodules of many species contain *Rhizobium* bacteria that fix nitrogen. The hard, colorful seeds of some species serve as jewelry items.

Diversity—World: approx. 17,000; **Costa Rica:** 565; **Monteverde:** 119

See page listings under **Fabaceae** in index for local examples.

55

Oreopanax xalapensis
Araliaceae – Ginseng family

Cacho de venado
"Deer antlers"

Description. A medium (rarely large) tree (5–25 m); LEAVES medium to very large, alternate and bunched at twig tips, long petioles of differing lengths with 5–10 leaflets, the lance-shaped leaflets usually without teeth in adults, but often toothed in saplings; dioecious; tiny white FLOWERS in round heads on stout terminal spikes; FRUIT a 1 cm purple-black berry (pale green immature) with 3–6 seeds.

Habitat and Phenology. Common in secondary forest and edge, particularly on ridges and cliff edges, and occasionally found in light gaps in mature forest. FL: JUL–OCT; FR: NOV–JAN.

Similar species. This is one of the most conspicuous trees because of the large, palmately compound leaves that look superficially like *Cecropia* leaves, but with the leaflets pointed and divided to the base. Trees with similar leaves include *Casimiroa edulis* (3–5 pubescent leaflets, fruits large balls), *Schefflera rodrigueziana* (formerly identified as *Didymopanax pittieri*) with small, almost round leaflets on long petiolules, occurring above 1550 m, *Schefflera robusta* (epiphytic shrub above 1500 m), and *Tabebuia rosea* (only 5 leaflets, large pink-white flowers, fruit a dangling cylindrical pod, below 900 m). Several other species of *Oreopanax* with similar flowers and fruits occur here, but these have simple leaves and usually grow as hemi-epiphytes.

Comments. Although the plants are dioecious, male and female flowers are very similar in appearance. They attract generalized diurnal pollinators such as stingless bees, flies and wasps. The fruits are dispersed by birds, especially the mountain robin and black-faced solitaire.

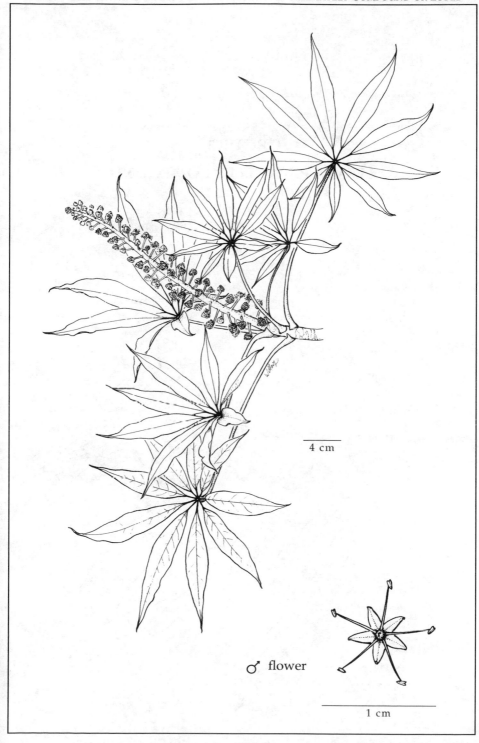

4 cm

♂ flower

1 cm

GROUP 3.
LEAVES PINNATELY COMPOUND

young *Cedrela* leaf

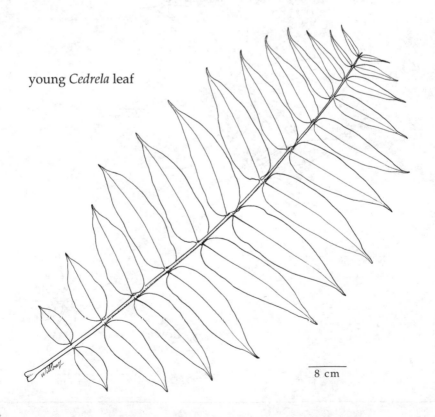

8 cm

Cedrela tonduzii

Meliaceae – Mahogany family

Cedro dulce

Tropical sweet cedar

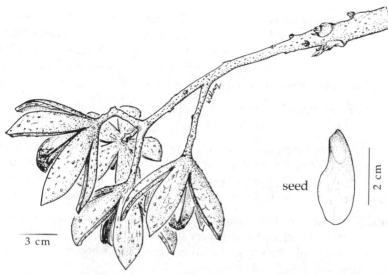

seed

2 cm

3 cm

Description. A large canopy tree (20–40 m); BARK with vertical fissures and cross cracks making a distinctive checkered pattern; LEAVES large (0.5–1 m long), alternate, with about 10–15 pairs of opposite leaflets 15–20 cm long, usually lacking a terminal leaflet, the leaflets lance-shaped, margin without teeth, briefly deciduous; dioecious; small yellow-green FLOWERS with a burnt garlic fragrance; FRUIT a 6 cm woody capsule with 5 valves that open on the tree to release numerous flat, winged seeds.

Habitat and Phenology. Occasional to rare in mature forest at 1300–1500 m; remnant individuals often left in pastures; more common on the Atlantic slope. FL: MAR–MAY; FR: JAN–FEB.

Similar species. *Cedrela salvadorensis*, with fruits about two times larger, grows on the Pacific slope at 700–1200 m. *C. odorata* (cedro amargo) with smaller fruits and much smaller leaflets, is common along the road to the Inter-American highway below 500 m.

Comments. This is probably the largest tree in the area, commonly exceeding a meter in trunk diameter. Most of the remaining large individuals are hollow, the solid ones having been cut for lumber. The huge, buttressed stumps are still encountered in the forests and pastures of the Monteverde community. The wood is soft, light, easy to work, and somewhat resistant to insects—good for cabinets and paneling. The lowland cedro amargo, with a higher quality wood, has been heavily exploited commercially. Both species have flowers that produce a strong onion/garlic fragrance at night and attract small moths and beetles.

Cupania glabra {Cascuá}

Sapindaceae – Soapberry family

Description. A subcanopy tree (10–20 m); LEAVES with the leaflets alternate, 10–14 per leaf, with marginal teeth, glabrous, the last leaflet subapical, and a short pointed spur at tip of rachis; dioecious; tiny 5-parted white FLOWERS; FRUIT a 1.5–2 cm capsule, brown with beige warts, opening in 3 valves to expose 1–3 brown-black seeds with a bright orange aril.

Habitat and Phenology. Most common in disturbed forest and edges from 1200–1450 m. FL: JAN, APR–MAY, JUL; FR: NOV.

Similar species. The large, compound leaves are similar to those of *Cedrela tonduzii*, though smaller. Even when the leaflets are even-numbered, there is a single terminal leaflet. This is the only *Cupania* in the area covered in this book, but several others occur in the region. All have alternate leaflets.

Comments. The unisexual flowers are pollinated by bees and wasps. The arillate seeds are strikingly colored and attract at least eight species of birds. The newly flushed leaves are often tinged with orange. The wood is pinkish and used as firewood as it splits easily with an ax.

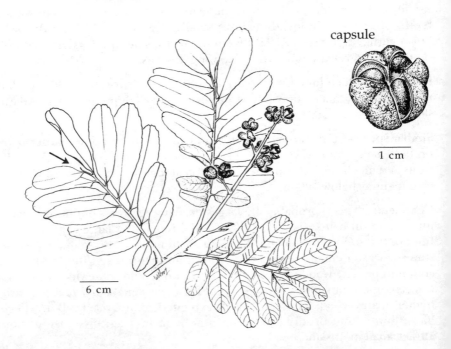

capsule

1 cm

6 cm

Guarea kunthiana *Cocora*

Meliaceae – Mahogany family

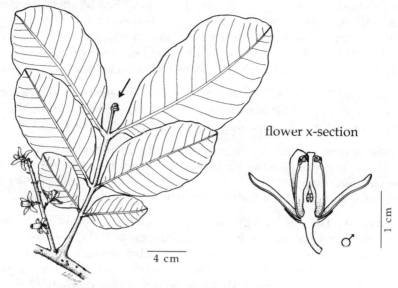

flower x-section

4 cm

1 cm

Description. A medium to large canopy tree (10–30 m); LEAVES large, 0.3–1 m long, the leaflets to 10 x 20 cm, glabrous, the tip of the leaf rachis with a persistent upturned bud; dioecious; FLOWERS 1 cm, cream-white with 4 petals curled back from a square central tube bearing 8 tiny anthers along its inner margin, fragrant, male and female nearly identical; FRUIT to 7 cm, yellow brown, opening with 4 thick leathery valves exposing 4 seeds covered with red arils.

Habitat and Phenology. Common in mature cloud forest and swamp at 1500–1700 m and down to 800 m on the Atlantic slope. FL: MAR, JUN; FR: MAY–JUL.

Similar species. This is one of the largest diameter trees of the high cloud forest. An understory species, *G.* cf. *tuisana*, with similar leaves and equally large fruits is common on the Atlantic slope. Four other *Guarea* species occur on the Pacific slope in our area. All have smaller leaves and fruits, which are often red or orange when mature. We still do not have reliable identifications of all of the local species.

Comments. All species of *Guarea* share the distinctive characteristic of having a leaf bud at the tip of the rachis. This bud produces second year growth of a new compound leaf. Eventually, the original leaflets drop off and the old petioles and midveins appear twig-like. The fragrant flowers are often seen on the ground beneath the tree. The arillate seeds are eaten by black guans and emerald toucanets. As with other members of this family, the wood is workable and makes attractive furniture.

61

Inga sierrae — *Guabo peludo*
Fabaceae – Legume family — "Hairy guava"
(Mimosoideae – Mimosa subfamily)

Description. A medium to large tree (10–25 m); LEAVES alternate, even-pinnate with the midvein winged, 2–4 pairs of leaflets to 12 x 18 cm, thick and stiff, concave below, rough pubescent, a nectar gland between each pair of leaflets; FLOWERS 4 cm, white and brush-like, a sweet fragrance at night; FRUIT a dark brown, densely pubescent pod, 3–4 cm wide by 10–20 cm long.

Habitat and Phenology. Common in pastures and forest edge, rarely a canopy tree with a straight bole in mature forest at 1200–1450 m; only on the Pacific slope. FL: SEP–FEB, sporadic in other months; FR: MAY–OCT.

Similar species. Other area *Inga* species with pubescent leaves include *I. tonduzii* with larger stipules and stalked nectaries and *I. micheliana* with scale-like stipules and sessile nectar glands. *I. oerstediana* with scale-like stipules, sessile nectaries, and cylindrical fruits occurs below 1200 m on both slopes.

Comments. The stiff, dark green, convex leaflets are conspicuous. The flowers attract hawk moths at night and hummingbirds during the day. *Inga* fruits are typically woody pods that do not dehisce, but are torn open by mammals (including children), who eat the white cottony aril tightly enveloping the seeds. Do not eat the seeds! They may be poisonous. (Formerly *I. brenesii.*)

Pithecellobium costaricense — *Cabello de angel*
(= *Cojoba costaricensis*)
Fabaceae – Legume family — "Angel's hair"
(Mimosoideae – Mimosa subfamily)

Description. A subcanopy tree (5–15 m); fern-like LEAVES twice compound, with 4–8 pairs of pinnae, each with 7–13 pairs of tiny leaflets (to 10 x 20 mm); small white brush-like FLOWERS in round heads; FRUIT a red, beaded pod twisting into a spiral to expose several shiny black seeds that have no aril.

Habitat and Phenology. Occurring sporadically in mature forest from 1400–1600 m and on the Atlantic slope. FL: FEB–APR (sporadic at other times); FR: MAR, AUG–SEP, (sporadic from JUN–FEB).

Similar species. This is the only tree with fern-like leaves found above 1200 m in our area. It often grows on ridges and hilltops exposed to the trade winds. All of the other *Pithecellobium* species in the region have much larger leaflets. *P.* (*Zygia*) *palmanum* has flat pods produced along the trunk and branches; *P.* (*Cojoba*) *catenatum* and *valerioi* have red twisted pods.

Comments. A small nectar gland is located on the midrib between each pair of leaflets. The nocturnal flowers are pollinated by moths. The twisted, bright red pods (immature, pinkish tan) are highly visible. Although the seeds lack arils, they are presumably dispersed by birds. The wood is hard.

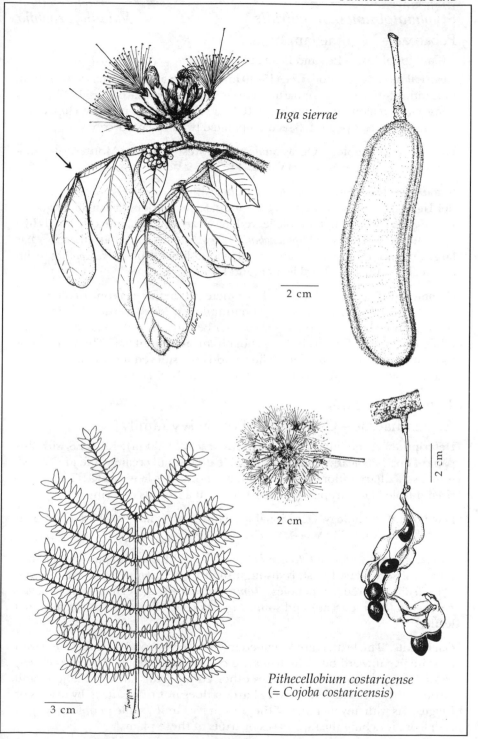

Inga sierrae

2 cm

2 cm

2 cm

Pithecellobium costaricense
(= *Cojoba costaricensis*)

3 cm

Styphnolobium monteviridis   *Vainillo, Frijolillo*
Fabaceae – Legume family
(Papilionoideae – Pea and Bean subfamily)

Description. A large canopy tree (15–40 m); LEAVES alternate, spiraled, to 30 cm long with 12–17 alternate or partly opposite leaflets; 2 cm lavender FLOWERS in dense clusters along the branches; FRUIT a yellow-brown, rubbery, elliptic pod with a long narrow point; 1–3 seeds, separated by deep constrictions.

Habitat and Phenology. Occasional in wet forest from the Monteverde community to the upper San Luis Valley. FL: FEB–MAR; FR: AUG–OCT.

Similar species. *Ormosia cruenta*, a legume with scarlet seeds common at Bajo del Tigre, has similar leaves with larger and fewer leaflets and small, flat pods. *Casearia sylvestris*, though simple-leaved, has leafy twigs that look strikingly like the compound leaves of *Styphnolobium*. *Picrasma excelsa*(Simaroubaceae) has larger, membranous leaflets and small, round black fruits. *Picramnia* species are treelets with small basal leaflets and bitter bark.

Comments. This tree, which reaches a meter in diameter, is one of 35 species of trees new to science that have been found near Monteverde. The fragrant flowers attract large bees such as carpenter bees (*Xylocopa*). The jelly-like aril filling the inside of the fruit skin probably attracts monkeys. The fruit skin is too leathery for birds to open. The wood is considered low in quality and is heavily attacked by long-horned beetles (Cerambycidae).

Tapirira mexicana   *Cirrí*
Anacardiaceae – Cashew and Poison ivy family

Description. A medium to large canopy tree (20–30 m); LEAVES with 2–4 pairs of opposite leaflets plus a terminal leaflet; small cream-white FLOWERS in dense axillary inflorescences hidden among the leaves; FRUIT an olive-sized purple-black drupe with a hard stone in a fibrous covering.

Habitat and Phenology. Occasional in mature forest at 1300–1600 m; also on the Atlantic slope. FL: MAR–MAY; FR: MAY–JUN.

Similar species. *Mauria heterophylla* ("Cirrí amarillo"), a smaller tree characteristic of secondary forest, is distinguished from *Tapirira* by its small red to black fruits and reddish petioles. *Tapirira* also looks superficially like *Exothea paniculata* (Sapindaceae) and some *Inga* species, all with a pair of terminal leaflets.

Comments. The leaflets are V-shaped in cross section and are often held with a distinctive upward tilt. The fruits are considered edible. *Tapirira* is closely related to *Spondias*, which includes other edible fruits such as the jobo and jocote. Although the wood is very hard, it does not resist attack by insects or fungus. As with any member of the poison ivy family, some people may get a rash from touching the sap, leaves or fruits of these plants.

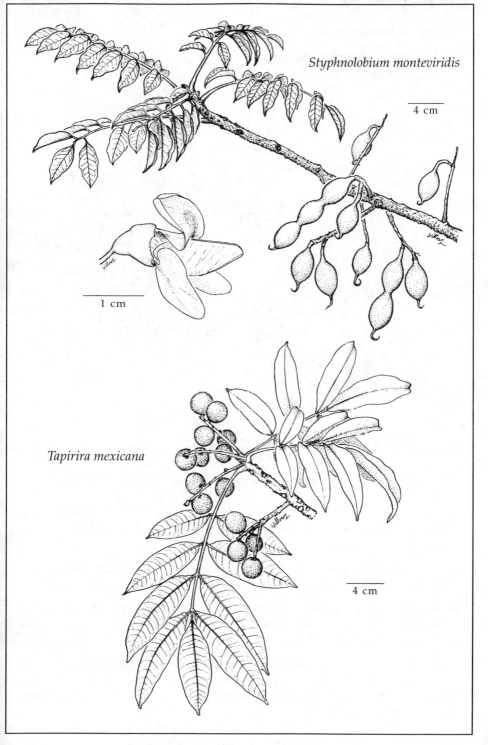

Styphnolobium monteviridis

4 cm

1 cm

Tapirira mexicana

4 cm

Trichilia havanensis *Uruca*

Meliaceae – Mahogany family

3 cm

Description. A medium tree (8–20 m); odd pinnate, glabrous LEAVES with 3–4 pairs of opposite leaflets plus a terminal leaflet, with blunt tips and inconspicuous lateral veins, without teeth, highly variable in size, but with petiole and rachis averaging 6–10 cm, rachis distinctly ridged on each side; dioecious; small 5-parted white FLOWERS in short axillary inflorescences, fused stamen filaments forming a short tube; FRUIT a 3-lobed, smooth brown capsule with red arillate seeds.

Habitat and Phenology. Widespread and common on Pacific slope from 1200–1600 m; also on Atlantic slope. FL: MAR–MAY; FR: APR–MAY, DEC–FEB.

Similar species. *Ruagea glabra* (Meliaceae), occurring in cloud forest above 1500 m, has many more leaflets and these are alternate. *Zanthoxylum melanostictum* has similar leaves with translucent dots.

Comments. This species can be found both in primary forest and in pastures. It is planted along some of the avenues in downtown San José (Parque Morazán). The flowers attract *Trigona* bees. The seeds are dispersed by birds. Uruca wood is relatively soft and white and easily worked.

MELIACEAE—Mahogany family

Field characters: *alternate, pinnately compound leaves with an even number of leaflets (except Trichilia), sweet bark odor, flowers with a staminal tube, fruit capsules with either arillate or winged seeds.*

The Meliaceae is a small family consisting mostly of trees and a few treelets. Most species have alternate pinnate leaves (a few have only one leaflet), either even-pinnate (*Cedrela, Guarea*) or odd-pinnate (*Ruagea, Trichilia*). The bark may have a faint sweet odor, or a garlic-onion odor in *Cedrela*. The flowers are mostly small, white to cream, and arranged in axillary inflorescences or occasionally on the trunk and branches (*Guarea*). Most species are dioecious. The corolla consists of 4–5 petals that fuse at the base. A staminal tube made up of fused stamen filaments is characteristic for the entire family. The stamens are usually equal to or twice the number of corolla lobes. The style often has a disc-shaped stigma. In our area, the fruits are of two types: dehiscent woody capsules with either arillate, bird-dispersed seeds (*Guarea, Ruagea, Trichilia*) or with winged, wind-dispersed seeds (*Cedrela*).

The pollinators of our species fall into two groups: small bees (*Trichilia*) and nocturnal lepidoptera and beetles (*Cedrela, Guarea*). The flowers of *Cedrela* produce a strong garlic-like odor. The fruits of *Guarea, Ruagea* and *Trichilia* open on the tree to expose seeds with red or orange arils that attract birds. Wind-dispersed seeds occur in *Cedrela* of our area and mahogany, which grows along the lower end of the Monteverde road to the Inter-American Highway.

The Meliaceae are abundant in the tropics. Many species of Meliaceae are important sources of fine wood. The best-known of these from Costa Rica are mahogany (*Swietenia*) and tropical or Spanish cedar (*Cedrela*). *Cedrela* produces an aromatic wood with a fine grain that is easy to work and resistant to insect attack (ideal for moth-proof chests). Recently, *Carapa guianensis* (caobilla) has become popular. *Guarea* is used to a more limited extent as lumber in Costa Rica.

Species Diversity—World: 575; **Costa Rica:** 34; **Monteverde:** 15

See page listings under **Meliaceae** in index
for local examples.

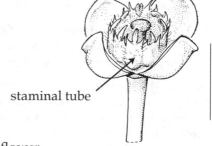

staminal tube

5 mm

Trichilia flower

Weinmannia pinnata   *Lorito*
Cunoniaceae – Cunonia family   "Little parrot"

Description. A large canopy tree (15–35 m); rounded STIPULES at twig tips; LEAVES 5–10 cm long, opposite, with 3–9 pairs of leaflets with toothed margins, the rachis broadly winged; small white FLOWERS on axillary spikes, fragrant in the day; FRUIT a small pointed capsule with minute wind-dispersed seeds.

Habitat and Phenology. Occasional in mature forest and edge at 1500–1700 m and more common on slopes exposed to the trade winds; occurring down to 800 m on the Atlantic side. FL: AUG–NOV; FR: NOV–FEB.

Similar species. The small, lacy pinnate leaves are hard to confuse with any other tree. Another species, *Weinmannia wercklei*, with very similar flowers, but simple leaves, is also common in the cloud forest. Both have conspicuous round stipules. A third, still unidentified species with three leaflets is found in the Quebrada Gata area of the Peñas Blancas valley.

Comments. The hard wood is marbled tan and black with white streaks. It is suitable for general house construction and has been used for making steps on trails in the Preserve. Trees sheltered from the wind may reach 80 cm in diameter, while those on the exposed peaks and ridges are usually smaller. In the elfin forest, this species usually begins life as an epiphyte.

Zanthoxylum fagara   *Limoncillo*
Rutaceae – Rue and Citrus family   "Little lemon"

Description. A small to medium tree (6–15 m); TRUNK with stout thorns; LEAVES 5–8 cm long, with 8–11 leaflets, usually odd-numbered, but often paired at the apex, dentate but the teeth often inconspicuous, with yellow translucent dots; the rachis finely winged; dioecious; tiny white FLOWERS on short axillary inflorescences; FRUIT a small, globose 2-valved capsule, opening to expose a single shiny black seed.

Habitat and Phenology. Common in old pastures, fence rows and secondary forest below 1400 m. FL: FEB–MAR?; FR: MAR–MAY?.

Similar species. *Matayba oppositifolia* (Sapindaceae) has superficially similar leaves and flowers, but the fruits are 3-lobed and the midvein is not winged. *Weinmannia pinnata* (see above) has a broadly winged midvein.

Comments. The leaves have a strong citrus odor. This species is abundant on the drier ridges below Monteverde, e.g., at Bajo del Tigre. A large individual grows next to the co-op grocery store in Monteverde. The heartwood is pink and the sapwood white. The live heartwood is susceptible to termite attack. It is used commonly for fence posts because the wood is resistant to rotting. It is also favored for living fences because the sparse foliage allows grass to grow beneath its crown. It was formerly known as *Z. insulare.*

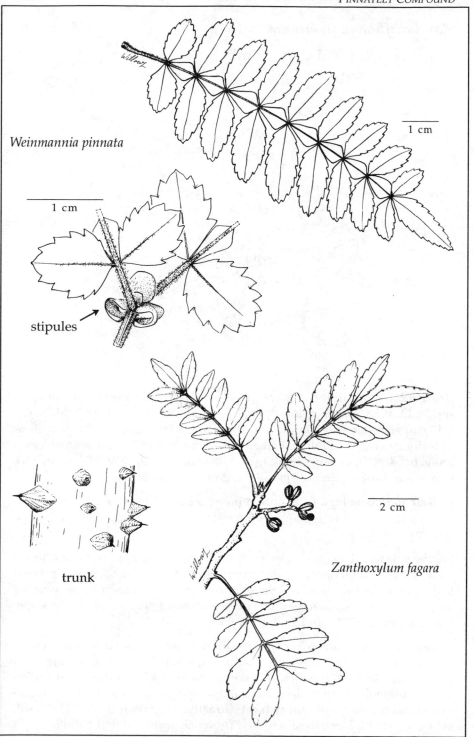

Weinmannia pinnata

1 cm

1 cm

stipules

trunk

2 cm

Zanthoxylum fagara

Zanthoxylum juniperinum *Lagartillo*

Rutaceae – Rue and Citrus family

2 cm

Description. An understory tree (4–8 m); TRUNK with volcano-shaped spines; LEAVES alternate, mostly even-pinnate with 2–3 pairs of leaflets to 5 x 12 cm, glabrous with inconspicuously toothed margins, translucent yellow dots along margin, minute red oil glands on the leaf surface, shredded leaves aromatic; dioecious; tiny white FLOWERS with 4 petals; FRUIT a 6 mm globose red to brown capsule, opening in 2 valves; 1 hard, black seed.

Habitat and Phenology. Common in moist areas at 1400–1600 m; occasional in moist ravines below 1400 m. FL: NOV–MAY, JUN–AUG (sporadic); FR: DEC–MAR, MAY.

Similar species. Two other species of *Zanthoxylum* occur in the cloud forest above 1500 m. Both have a single terminal leaflet and smooth, non-expressed leaf veins, while the veins of Z. *juniperinum* are slightly raised. The leaves of Z. *fagara* (see previous page), which occurs below 1400 m on the Pacific slope, have a terminal leaflet and a winged rachis.

Comments. Like many other species of Rutaceae, *Zanthoxylum* is dioecious. The tiny, white flowers primarily attract wasps, which appear to be the main pollinators. In fruit, this can be a conspicuous treelet in the forest understory. Although the seeds have no aril and appear inedible, they are apparently coated with a nutrient-rich oil attractive to certain birds. The hard, yellow wood with black streaks is used for fence posts and tool handles.

RUTACEAE—Rue and Citrus family

Field characters: *compound leaves (either alternate or opposite) with translucent dots OR simple alternate leaves with translucent dots, a citrus odor in torn leaves, small radially symmetric white flowers in inflorescences, dehiscent fruits. Trunk often spiny.*

The Rutaceae is made up of a diversity of life forms ranging from herbs to canopy trees. It is even more diverse vegetatively. Although the majority of species have compound leaves, which are either alternate or opposite, these may be pinnate, palmate, or trifoliolate (with 3 leaflets), and often they are reduced to a single leaflet. Many species also have simple alternate leaves. The most consistent vegetative character is the presence of minute translucent oil glands (pellucid dots) in the leaf blade or along its edge, with an aromatic citrus odor upon being crushed. One of the largest genera of trees, *Zanthoxylum*, generally has thick spines on the trunk. The flowers, in axillary inflorescences, are mostly small and white, radially symmetric, with a 4–5-parted calyx and corolla, and usually 8–10 stamens. The ovary often has deep lobes equal to the number of petals. Dioecy is common among the tree species. A few genera outside of our area have larger flowers (*Toxosiphon*) and a few have tubular corollas (*Galipea*). The fruits are mostly dry dehiscent follicles (*Zanthoxylum*), but a few drupes (*Stauranthus*) and multi-seeded fleshy fruits (*Casimiroa*) also belong to this family.

The species in the Monteverde area all have small white flowers pollinated by bees and wasps, but species with tubular white flowers (*Galipea*) that are presumably moth-pollinated occur in other parts of Costa Rica. The 2-valved fruits of *Zanthoxylum* open to present a single seed that is bird-dispersed; however, these fruits attract flocks of parrots that devastate the fruit crops before they mature. *Stauranthus* fruits are purple-black drupes very similar to those of *Tapirira* and the Lauraceae. The fruit of *Casimiroa* is a large fleshy ball with several large seeds surrounded by a sweet edible pulp eaten by mammals.

The family name comes from rue (*Ruta*), a widely grown herb with medicinal uses. The most important commercial species of Rutaceae are the members of the genus *Citrus*, which includes oranges, lemons and grapefruit, and kumquats (*Fortunella* spp.). A number of species produce medicinal oils and spices and a few are grown as flowering ornamentals. Only a very small number of species provide timber. The wood of a few species of *Zanthoxylum* is used in our area for specialty items such as tool handles and gate posts because it is very hard and durable. Recently, the bitter chemicals in the rind of citrus fruits have shown some potential as natural insecticides.

Species Diversity—World: 1700; **Costa Rica:** 36; **Monteverde:** 14

See page listings under **Rutaceae** in index for local examples.

GROUP 4.

LEAVES OPPOSITE OR WHORLED WITH PROMINENT INTERPETIOLAR STIPULES

RUBIACEAE—Madder and Coffee family

Field characters: *simple, opposite, entire leaves, interpetiolar stipules, flowers with inferior ovary and 4–6-lobed corolla fused into a tube.*

The Rubiaceae is a large and extremely diverse family including plants of all growth habits from herbs to canopy trees and woody lianas to epiphytes. Nevertheless, a few key characters make recognition fairly easy: simple, opposite leaves without teeth and leaf-like stipules that cross the stem between the leaf bases. A very few similar species are found in Caprifoliaceae (*Viburnum*), Malpighiaceae (*Malpighia*), and Rhizophoraceae (*Cassipourea*). With an inferior ovary the flowers and fruits are also distinctive. The calyx and corolla have 4–6 lobes with an equal number of stamens. The corolla is fused into a tube with the stamens attached inside it. The stigma forks into two conspicuous lobes. Many species are dioecious or heterostylous. The fruits are highly diverse, ranging from fleshy drupes and berries, which are attractive to animals, to capsules with wind-dispersed seeds. However, all of them have a characteristic calyx scar or persistent calyx lobes at the fruit tip, indicating their origin from an inferior ovary.

The Rubiaceae are prominent members of all tropical forests. In Costa Rica, the "rubes" (e.g., *Hoffmannia*, *Psychotria*) are among the five most abundant families represented in the understory of most forests, and a few species are common in second growth and edges (*Gonzalagunia*, *Guettarda*, *Palicourea*). The great majority of species are pollinated either by bees in the daytime or by Lepidoptera (including hawk moths) at night. The magnificent fragrances of some of these nocturnal flowers could have potential as perfumes. A number of species with red or yellow flowers (*Hamelia*, *Hillia*, *Palicourea*) attract hummingbirds as pollinators.

The most important Rubiaceae in cultivation are species of coffee (*Coffea arabica*, etc.), the world's main source of caffeine. While native to central Africa, three distinct species are cultivated in Costa Rica. Otherwise, the family supplies little of commercial value other than quinine (*Cinchona*), a drug that protects against malaria, and ipecac (*Cephaelis*)—an emetic alkaloid used to induce vomiting. A large number of ornamentals are cultivated for their showy or fragrant flowers including gardenia and ixora. Temperate members include bedstraw (*Galium*) and partridge berry (*Mitchella repens*).

Coffea

Diversity—World: 10,400; **Costa Rica:** ca. 410; **Monteverde:** 148

See next seven pages for local examples of **Rubiaceae**.

Cosmibuena valerii
Rubiaceae – Madder and Coffee family

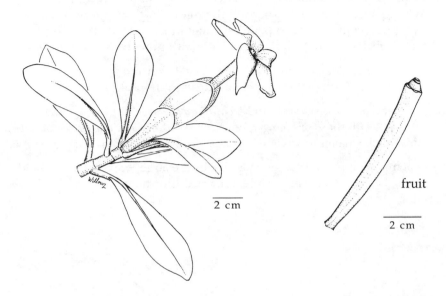

2 cm

fruit

2 cm

Description. A medium tree or large hemi-epiphyte (5–10 m); LEAVES to 4 x 11 cm, spatula-shaped, fleshy and smooth, large paddle-shaped stipules; long tubular white FLOWERS to 8 cm, 5-lobed with margin red on the underside; FRUIT a long, cylindrical capsule containing numerous tiny, wind-dispersed seeds.

Habitat and Phenology. Locally common in elfin forest and on the highest peaks and exposed ridges at 1550–1800 m. FL: MAY–AUG; FR: MAR–APR.

Similar species. *Cosmibuena grandiflora* grows as a medium-sized tree on narrow rock ridges on the driest parts of the Pacific slope at 1000–1200 m (Bajo del Tigre). It has shorter flowers that lack the red margin. *C. valerii* was previously included in the genus *Hillia*. Several species of *Hillia* are also found at Monteverde, all of which have much smaller flowers and grow as epiphytic shrubs.

Comments. The erect, scarlet-tipped buds and white pinwheel flowers with red-bordered lobes produced singly at the twig tips are unique to the area. Like some of the clusias, this species grows as a hemi-epiphytic shrub in forest sheltered from the trade winds at lower elevations, but acts like a tree in the elfin forest and on exposed peaks and ridges. The flowers produce a strong, sweet scent at night that attracts hawk moths. Up close, one can easily recognize the 3–5 cm spatulate stipules.

Elaeagia auriculata

Rubiaceae – Madder and Coffee family

Description. A subcanopy tree (8–20 m); TWIGS angular with 4 ridges; large LEAVES to 30 x 50 cm, widest beyond the middle with an abruptly narrowed tip, soft pubescent, very short petioles; small white FLOWERS in large inflorescences; FRUIT a small, dark red capsule with numerous minute seeds.

Habitat and Phenology. Common in open cloud forest and gaps at 1550–1700 m. FL: extended flowering: JAN–FEB (peak); FR: APR–JUL (peak).

Similar species. *Ficus macbridei* and *Sloanea ampla* have large leaves that could be confused with those of *Elaeagia*, but they are alternate. *Elaeagia uxpanapensis*, with much smaller leaves and stipules, occurs only on the Atlantic slope.

Comments. This tree is easy to recognize by the large, opposite leaves held at an upward angle and a pair of large, terminal, (intrapetiolar) paddle-shaped stipules.

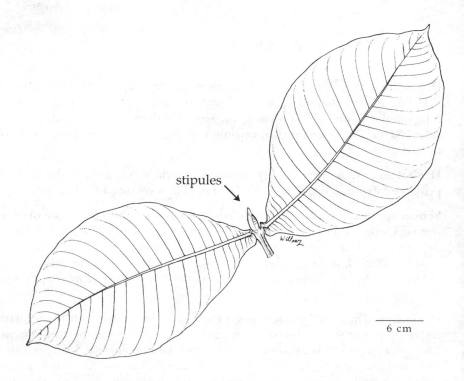

stipules

6 cm

74

Gonzalagunia rosea
Rubiaceae – Madder and Coffee family

Maicillo

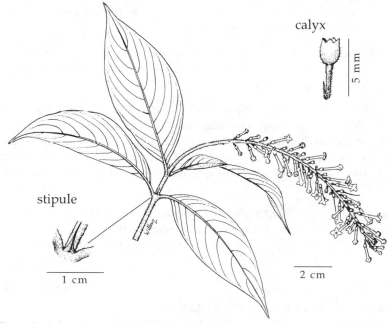

Description. A treelet (3–6 m); with pubescent lance-shaped LEAVES to 4 x 9 cm, long pointed stipules; elongate pendant spikes at the twig tips bearing 1 cm long FLOWERS with a pink tube and 4 white lobes; small round white FRUIT, somewhat flattened, with a spongy texture; 4 seeds.

Habitat and Phenology. Common on road banks, forest edge, and second growth from 1500–1600 m; extending down the Atlantic slope. FL: APR–JUN; FR: JUN–JUL.

Similar species. On the Pacific slope, *Rondeletia monteverdensis* and *R. torresii*, with glabrous leaves, have flowers of similar size and shape on branched inflorescences; the flower tube is white, not pink; and the fruits are small capsules. *G. panamensis*, with smaller white flowers, grows below 1100 m. Three other species of *Gonzalagunia* are found on the Atlantic slope. Some *Cestrum* spp. (Solanaceae) also have spongy, white fruits, but their leaves are alternate.

Comments. The flowers attract a wide variety of visitors including hummingbirds, bees, butterflies and moths. The fruit belong to a "guild" of spongy, white, styrofoam-like fruits with little juice. The plant seems to expand these fruits to their mature size by puffing them up with air to make them look larger and more appetizing than they actually are. The fruits are eaten by many birds including black guans and prong-billed barbets. The plants are sometimes used as ornamental shrubs.

75

Guettarda poasana
Rubiaceae – Madder and Coffee family

Description. A small to medium tree (5–15 m); LEAVES to 9 x 17 cm with long petioles; extremely aromatic FLOWERS with 4 white lobes with lacy margins and a 2 cm tube, in scorpioid inflorescences; FRUIT a 1 cm blue-black berry with 1–2 seeds, on arching, forked branches.

Habitat and Phenology. Common in secondary forest, on road banks, and landslides in the cloud forest above 1500 m; also on the Atlantic slope. FL: MAY–SEP; FR: MAR–JUN.

Similar species. This tree can be positively identified by the lacy-margined corollas that fall to the ground. *Gonzalagunia rosea* has narrow, lance-shaped leaves and unbranched inflorescences, while *Guettarda* has broad leaves and the inflorescences are erect and branched. *Rondeletia torresii* is also similar vegetatively, but the flowers have entire corolla lobes and the fruits are small capsules.

Comments. The flowers have a pleasant, almost intoxicating fragrance that attracts hawk moths at night. Hummingbirds and skipper butterflies visit the flowers in the early morning and evening. The fruits are eaten by birds.

Psychotria elata *Labios de novia*
Rubiaceae – Madder and Coffee family Hot lips

Description. An understory treelet (2–5 m); LEAVES to 6 x 15 cm, elliptic, glossy green above with raised lateral veins; small white tubular FLOWERS emerging from a mass of green bracts grouped between a pair of large, red, showy bracts; FRUIT an elongate blue-black berry with 2 seeds.

Habitat and Phenology. Common in the cloud forest understory at 1500–1600 m. FL: all year, but more vigorous in wet season; FR: all year, sporadic.

Similar species. *Psychotria chiriquiensis* with similar leaves, but purple bracts, occurs at higher elevations, especially those exposed to the trade winds. Many other "rubes," such as *Palicourea*, have similar foliage, but lack the showy flower bracts.

Comments. The flowers are mainly pollinated by hummingbirds, but also attract *Heliconius* butterflies. This and related species were formerly placed in the genus *Cephaelis*.

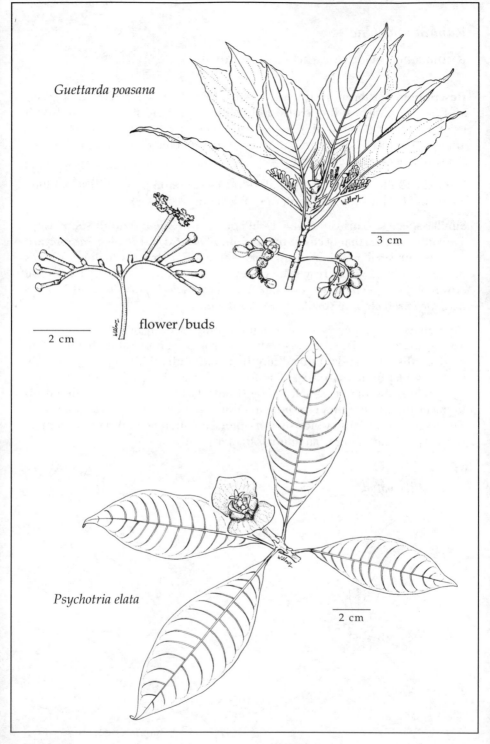

Guettarda poasana

3 cm

flower/buds

2 cm

Psychotria elata

2 cm

Randia matudae

Rubiaceae – Madder and Coffee family

Description. A subcanopy tree (10–20 m); LEAVES to 6 x 16 cm, dark green and fleshy, glabrous; dioecious; FLOWERS pinwheel-shaped with 4 or 5 twisted, narrow, pointed white lobes at the end of a 4 cm tube, very fragrant at night; the FRUIT is a hard ball to 7 cm in diameter, containing numerous flat seeds in a soft black matrix.

Habitat and Phenology. Occasional to locally common in wet forest at 1300–1500 m. FL: MAR–AUG; FR: most of year (mature FEB–MAY).

Similar species. This is the only local species of *Randia* without spiny twigs. Two other species that occur in the region, *R. brenesii* and *R.* near *calycosa*, are treelets with smaller, bright orange fruits that attract birds, which peck holes in the hard fruit wall to reach the gooey, black seed mass inside. The dense crown of dark green leaves and large fruit recall *Salacia petenensis* and *Posoqueria latifolia*, which have smaller leaves and fruit.

Comments. This species was not named until 1988. It occurs in Mexico as well as Costa Rica. The flowers produce a strong fragrance at night attracting hawk moths (Sphingidae) that drain the nectar with their long tongues while hovering like hummingbirds. The female flowers have a bulbous, inferior ovary that is absent in the males. The flowers last for several days, then drop to the ground where they continue to emit a spoiled, sickish-sweet fragrance. The large, round fruits, which do not open, can often be found under female trees. We do not know what animals disperse the seeds.

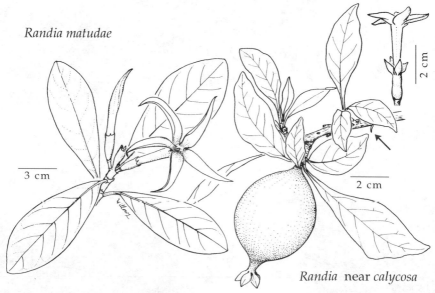

Randia matudae

3 cm

2 cm

2 cm

Randia near *calycosa*

Rondeletia monteverdensis

Rubiaceae – Madder and Coffee family

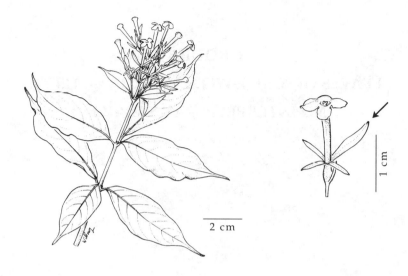

2 cm

1 cm

Description. A treelet (2–6 m); LEAVES to 3 x 8 cm, mostly 3 per node (whorled); small white FLOWERS with a 1.5 cm tube and 4 rounded white lobes, sepals of different lengths; FRUIT a 5 mm brown capsule with numerous tiny black seeds.

Habitat and Phenology. Common in disturbed habitats and larger light gaps along the Continental Divide near La Ventana and on the higher peaks (1550–1800 m). FL: most of year, peak in MAY–JUN, AUG–OCT; FR: MAR–JUN.

Similar species. The leaves of other *Rondeletia* species are opposite, not whorled. *Rondeletia torresii* has larger, white flowers, those of *R. amoena* are pinkish-white with a yellow throat, and *R. buddleioides* has woolly beige leaf undersides and beige flowers. *Gonzalagunia rosea* is vegetatively similar to *Rondeletia*, but the leaves are paired, the sepals are all equal in length, and the inflorescences are long, pendant spikes.

Comments. The newly flushing leaves often have an orange cast. The calyx lobes (sepals) of *Rondeletia* spp. vary in size on each flower with one usually much longer than the others. Most *Rondeletia* species have nocturnal flowers that are pollinated by moths; however, the flowers of *R. amoena* are also visited by butterflies and long-tongued flies (Bombyliidae, Tabanidae) during the day.

GROUP 5.
LEAVES OPPOSITE WITH MARGINAL TEETH, NO INTERPETIOLAR STIPULES

Conostegia oerstediana
Melastomataceae – Melastome family

Lengua de vaca
"Cow's tongue"

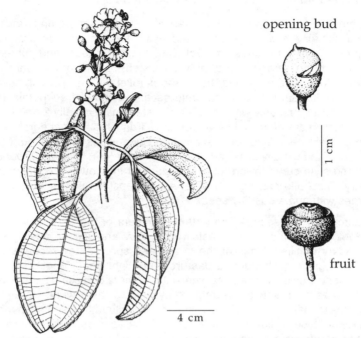

opening bud

1 cm

fruit

4 cm

Description. A medium-sized tree (8–20 m); LEAVES to 8 x 16 cm, oval, leathery, glabrous, the secondary veins arising 5–10 mm above the leaf base; FLOWERS 2 cm across with 8 white petals, and 24 orange anthers; FRUIT 1 cm, a dark purple, juicy berry with numerous tiny, brown, wedge-shaped seeds.

Habitat and Phenology. An abundant tree, typical of old pastures, secondary forest and forest edge at 1400–1700 m. FL: FEB–MAY; FR: MAY–SEP.

Similar species. The Melastomataceae is a large family with about 35 species at Monteverde. Several species of local *Conostegia* and *Miconia* have a similar general appearance to *C. oerstediana* and a technical key is needed to distinguish them. *C. rufescens*, with elliptic pubescent leaves, is a common light gap colonizer in the Preserve.

Comments. The delicately scented flowers produce no nectar. They are pollinated by female bees that vibrate the flowers to collect pollen from the anthers that open by terminal pores. The fruits are eaten by bats as well as 16 species of birds. This tree readily colonizes abandoned pastures and often develops nearly single species stands, such as those seen along the lower parts of the Río and Nuboso Trails in the Cloud Forest Preserve. This species was misidentified as *C. bernoulliana* in the past.

81

MELASTOMATACEAE—Melastome family

Field characters: *simple opposite leaves with secondary veins parallel to the margin and veins perpendicular to those, creating a net-like appearance, flowers with free petals and elbowed stamens.*

The melastomes comprise a large family mostly of shrubs and small trees, but it also contains herbs, climbers, and epiphytes. The leaves are opposite (rarely whorled and sometimes unequal) with or without teeth and pubescence, mostly elliptic to round and with a fairly consistent pattern of sub-parallel secondary veins that arise at the leaf base and parallel the margin. The flowers, in much-branched axillary or terminal inflorescences, have free petals ranging from 4 to 8, most commonly white or pink, the stamens (typically 2 or 3 times the number of petals) are often yellow and dehisce from small apical pores. The stamen filaments are often elbowed and have odd extensions at the bend. The style is unbranched and usually exserted. In some genera (e.g., *Blakea, Topobea*) the stamens and style curve toward opposite sides of the flower producing a slight asymmetry. The fruits can be either dehiscent capsules with minute seeds or juicy berries with numerous tiny seeds.

Melastomes are especially important members of the understory of many lowland wet forests and cloud forests where they are usually among the five most abundant families. Many of the larger tree species are secondary forest colonists that grow in abandoned pastures and light gaps. Bees pollinate the flowers of most species. In the case where the anthers dehisce by small terminal pores, the bees must shake the anthers by holding them while vibrating their wing muscles to make the pollen issue out in a tiny cloud that settles in the bee's body hair. This type of flower lacks nectar. Some species have dimorphic stamens: one set that produces pollen for pollination, and a larger, more colorful set that provides pollen for the bees' food, apparently directing the attention of pollinators away from the smaller stamens. The flowers of a few species (e.g., *Blakea chlorantha*) do produce nectar and these are visited by nimble arboreal mice that may be the main pollinators, though hummingbirds, bats and bees have been recorded visiting some of these species, also. The majority of our species produce juicy berries with small seeds dispersed by birds. The species with dry capsules are mostly weedy herbs and shrubs that simply drop their seeds onto the ground where they may be blown around by the wind.

The family is of little economic importance, although a number of species are ornamentals, such as glory bush (*Tibouchina*). Some *Conostegia* species have edible fruits. Most of the tree species are too small or soft-wooded to be valuable for timber. One species of *Mouriri* in our area (with a remarkable resemblance to Myrtaceae) is a canopy tree of primary forest.

Species Diversity—World: 4750, but especially diverse in the Neotropics; **Costa Rica:** approx. 259; **Monteverde:** 93

See previous and following pages for local examples of **Melastomataceae.**

82

Conostegia xalapensis

Melastomataceae – Melastome family

María

"Maria"

Description. A small to medium tree (2–20 m); BARK tan with vertical fissures; LEAVES to 3 x 8 cm, often of different sizes at a node, the underside with a conspicuous carpet of beige pubescence contrasting with the shiny green upper side, secondary veins parallel the margin and extend to leaf tip, margin with small, even teeth; FLOWERS 1.5 cm across, 5–7 white petals in a pinwheel pattern, anthers yellow; FRUIT a 1 cm, purple-black berry with many small seeds.

Habitat and Phenology. Abundant in secondary forest, edge habitat, and pastures in the drier parts of our area (1100–1450 m). This weedy tree readily invades old pastures. FL: FEB–AUG; FR: MAR–SEP.

Similar species. *Conostegia* is a large genus in Costa Rica with 12 species occurring in our area; however, the shiny green leaves with beige pubescence on the underside make it difficult to confuse María with any other local tree. The flower buds of *Conostegia* are sealed by a pointed cap formed by the fused sepals. When the flower opens, the calyx cap pops off and may remain hinged to the receptacle on one side.

Comments. The pattern of netted leaf venation (lateral veins paralleling the margin with short, parallel tertiary veins at right angles to the midvein) identifies the Melastomataceae. The fragrant flowers attract female bees that collect the pollen. Most melastome flowers produce no nectar. This species has potential for use as a living fence, while also providing food resources for bees and fruit-eating birds.

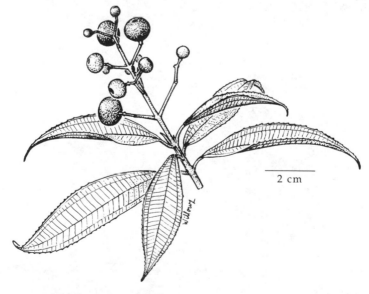

2 cm

83

Koanophyllon pittieri *Quitirrí*

Asteraceae – Aster and Composite family

Description. A treelet or small tree (2–10 m); LEAVES to 7 x 15 cm, margins with conspicuous (in sun) or sparse, inconspicuous teeth (in shade), glabrous; small brush-like white FLOWERS in 5 mm tall heads on terminal inflorescences; FRUIT a 2 mm dry, black achene with a beige pappus (a tuft of hairs for wind dispersal).

Habitat and Phenology. Common in the understory of primary forest and occasional on forest edges at 1400–1600 m, but most abundant around 1500 m. FL: AUG–OCT (sporadic all year); FR: OCT–MAY.

Similar species. A closely related species, *K. hylonomum*, which flowers in March, is common in ravines lower on the Pacific slope (1200–1400 m).

Comments. This species is inconspicuous until it flowers, and then one realizes that it is one of the most abundant treelets in the understory and light gaps of the cloud forest. As in other members of the tribe Eupatoriae, the heads contain only disk flowers; the petal-like ray flowers are absent. The seeds have a hairy wing (pappus) for wind dispersal.

3 cm

Montanoa guatemalensis — Tubú
Asteraceae – Aster and Composite family — Tubú

Description. A small to medium tree (3–15 m); TRUNK with deeply striated beige bark; LEAVES to 13 x 17 cm, with 2–4 shallow lobes, underside with fine pubescence; inflorescences of large heads (5 cm across), the outer ray FLOWERS white, to 2.5 cm long, the inner disk flowers orange; FRUIT a 3 mm dry, brown wingless seed.

Habitat and Phenology. Found in scattered patches along the driest ridge tops on the Pacific slope below Monteverde at 1000–1200 m. FL: DEC–JAN; FR: JAN–FEB.

Similar species. *M. tomentosa*, with smaller flowers and very pubescent leaves, flowers from Nov–Jan. It occurs naturally on the Pacific slope at 800–1000 m and is also cultivated in hedge rows on local farms.

Comments. In recent years, Tubú has been planted extensively for windbreaks throughout the area. It can now be seen with its large, daisy-like flowers as high as 1500 m. The outer, petal-like, white flowers (ray flowers) are sterile; the hard, round seeds, which lack a pappus, are produced only by the orange flowers in the center of the head (disk flowers). They apparently drop to the ground where they are dispersed by rodents. The wood is used for long-lived, small-diameter posts.

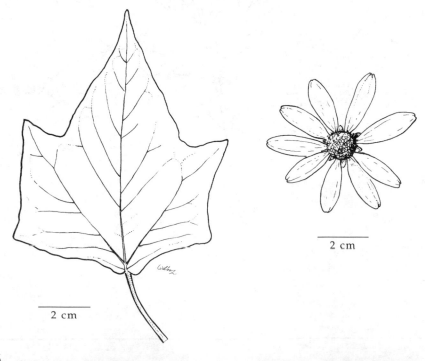

2 cm

2 cm

86

Neomirandea angularis

Asteraceae – Aster and Composite family

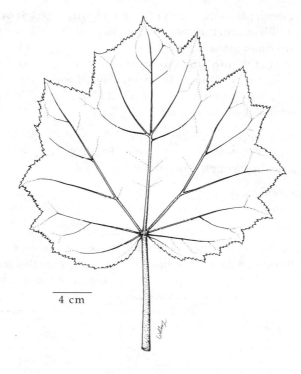

4 cm

Description. A small tree (4–8 m); large, broad LEAVES to 40 cm long with serrate margin and tooth-like lobes, rough pubescent; lavender-blue brush-like FLOWERS in large inflorescences; FRUIT a small wind-borne black seed with a tuft of white hairs.

Habitat and Phenology. Common in roadside and second growth habitat at 1500–1700 m. FL: JUL–SEP; FR: SEP–DEC?

Similar species. When not flowering, this species can be confused with a less abundant composite in the same habitat, *Erato vulcanica*, which has smooth, fleshy lobed leaves and large, yellow flowers.

Comments. Although the large, maple-like leaves with long petioles are distinctive, the lavender-blue flowers are outstanding. This species is common along the road in the Preserve and at the Santa Elena Reserve. It becomes a dominant successional species in abandoned pastures on the upper Atlantic slope. The flowers often attract butterflies and diurnal moths (Ctenuchidae) on sunny mornings. Country people use the wood in construction of bird cages.

87

Siparuna tonduziana   *Limoncillo*
Monimiaceae – Monimia family   "Little lemon"

Description. A treelet (2–5 m); LEAVES to 8 x 18 cm, widest at or beyond the middle, margin with alternating large and small teeth, with dense pubescence of long hairs and small branched (stellate) hairs, a lemony odor in shredded leaves; dioecious; FLOWERS yellow to orange, 3 mm, top-shaped and without petals; FRUIT rose to red, 1.5 cm, teardrop-shaped with a depression at the tip, dehiscing into 5–6 recurved lobes, crushed fruit with a sharp lemony perfume odor; seeds black with a red aril.

Habitat and Phenology. Common in cloud forest light gaps and edges at 1500–1600 m. FL: FEB–MAR, JUN, OCT–NOV; FR: JUN, AUG, NOV, JAN (flower and fruit sporadically through most of year).

Similar species. Several other *Siparuna* species with less pubescent leaves, but similar flowers and fruits, occur in the area. All share the strongly scented leaves and fruits.

Comments. This treelet is usually noticed because of its large, opposite, hairy leaves and oddly shaped fruits. The limoncillo is always worth a pause to smell the pungent, perfumed scent of the leaves and fruits. Some species were used as a source of natural fragrances in the past for scenting soaps and perfumes. Because these plants are dioecious, we know they must be cross-pollinated; however, we have not observed the pollinators.

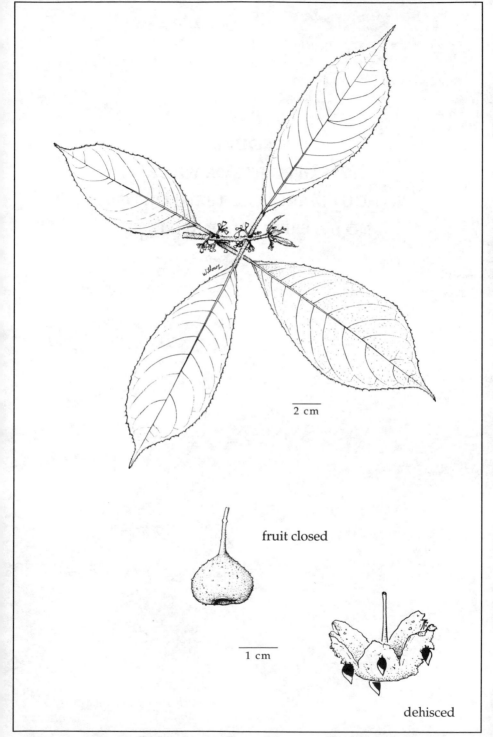

2 cm

fruit closed

1 cm

dehisced

GROUP 6.
LEAVES OPPOSITE OR WHORLED
WITHOUT MARGINAL TEETH OR LOBES,
NO INTERPETIOLAR STIPULES

3 cm

Bunchosia macrophylla

Bunchosia macrophylla
Malpighiaceae – Barbados cherry family

Description. A treelet (3–6 m); LEAVES to 11 x 26 cm, elliptic, entire, blade densely pubescent below (with T-shaped hairs); FLOWERS 1.5 cm across, 5 scoop-shaped yellow petals, fleshy, 5-lobed calyx with oil-secreting glands on outer surface; FRUIT 1.5–2 cm, bright orange, glabrous, with 1–2 smooth cream seeds.

Habitat and Phenology. Occasional in understory of primary and secondary forest; also on forest edges. FL: JAN, JUL–SEP (any month, not synchronized); FR: SEP–MAR, JUL.

Similar species. This tree belongs to a complex of closely related species that are not yet fully understood. We may well have two distinct species at Monteverde: one in the cloud forest and another in the drier forest on the Pacific slope. *Bunchosia veluticarpa* is a canopy tree with larger flowers and pubescent fruits found at 1300–1450 m. *Malpighia glabra* (at 900–1200 m) and *M. albiflora* (at 1400–1600 m) are two understory treelets with pink flowers and scarlet fruits.

Comments. *Bunchosia* is a showy and attractive treelet both when flowering and fruiting. The flowers of this family do not secrete nectar; instead, glands on the calyx lobes produce an oily secretion that is highly attractive to certain solitary bees, such as species of *Centris* (Apidae), that use these rich resources for feeding their larvae. Orange-bellied trogons have been seen eating the fruits.

bud, showing glandular calyx

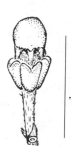

91

Chionanthus panamensis

Come negro

Oleaceae – Olive family

Description. A medium to large tree (20–30 m); TRUNK fluted with beige bark; LEAVES to 3 x 8 cm, elliptic, glabrous, with long petioles; 1 cm white FLOWERS with 4 narrow petals and only 2 stamens, fragrant at night; FRUIT a 1.5–2 cm fleshy elliptic cream-yellow drupe; seed almond-shaped.

Habitat and Phenology. Occasional in mature forest at 1200–1450 m. FL: FEB–APR; FR: OCT–NOV.

Similar species. *Chionanthus* can be readily identified by its light brown bark, fluted trunk and opposite, pointed leaves. With its small opposite leaves, this tree closely resembles some species of Myrtaceae. *Chionanthus oblanceolatus*, an understory tree with purple fruits, is common in parts of the Peñas Blancas valley.

Comments. The white, mass-flowering crowns are visible from a distance. The strongly scented, nocturnal flowers may be pollinated by small moths and beetles. The yellow drupes are eaten by band-tailed pigeons, emerald toucanets and three-wattled bellbirds. Formerly called *Linociera panamensis*, this species was common on the dry, forested ridges and hill tops between Monteverde and Tilarán; however, the species is now rare because of exploitation for its hardwood. The very hard, dark tan wood was used in building foundations, axe handles, beams, and the tongues and wheels of ox carts.

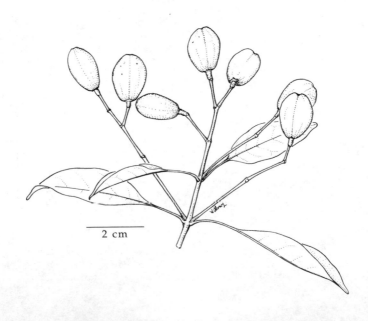

2 cm

92

Citharexylum costaricensis

Verbenaceae – Verbena and Lantana family

Dama

"Lady"

2 cm

Description. A medium tree (6–20 m); TRUNK with light brown, finely fissured bark; TWIGS square; LEAVES to 4 x 13 cm, narrowly elliptic, widest at or just below the middle, often V-shaped in x-section, glabrous, often toothed in saplings; dioecious; very small white 5-lobed FLOWERS in pendant terminal spikes, more fragrant at night, calyx not lobed; FRUITS 1 cm, round, orange when immature changing to brown-black when mature, 1-seeded.

Habitat and Phenology. Common in pastures, forest edge and secondary forest at 1100–1450 m. FL: JAN–MAY; FR: APR–JUN.

Similar species. Two other species occur here—*C. donnell-smithii* (a large, canopy tree with larger leaves and flat nectaries at the leaf base, and lobed calyx) occurs from 1300–1600 m, while *C. caudatum* (with leaf base curled under) grows from 1500–1700 m.

Comments. This is a fast-growing, successional tree. Noticeable because of its strong floral fragrance, it is visited by small moths at night and also by stingless bees during the day. The fruits are eaten by more than 20 species of birds. Extrafloral nectar glands located under the base of the leaf blade presumably attract ants. This tree is recommended as a living fence because in addition to supporting barbed wire, the flowers and fruits help to sustain local wildlife. The soft, white wood can be used as firewood while green.

93

Clusia stenophylla   *Azahar de monte, Copey*
Clusiaceae – Mangosteen and Garcinia family   Clusia

Description. A small tree or large epiphytic shrub (5–8 m); large, oval LEAVES to 9 x 20 cm, obovate with a rounded tip, margin entire, thick and stiff, exuding yellow latex when cut; dioecious; 2 cm white FLOWERS with 5–7 petals, fragrant; FRUIT a 2–3 cm green, rubbery capsule that opens into 5–7 canoe-shaped valves, each valve with a row of seeds covered by bright red-orange arils.

Habitat and Phenology. Occasional in pastures (usually growing on logs and stumps) or in the forest canopy at 1300–1500 m. FL: APR–MAY, NOV–DEC; FR: APR–MAY, AUG, NOV.

Similar species. Clusias superficially look like figs (*Ficus* spp.), but figs have alternate leaves. About a dozen species of *Clusia* occur in the region. Most are large epiphytic shrubs. An undescribed species very similar to *C. stenophylla* is a common terrestrial tree in the elfin forest and along the Continental Divide, and at lower elevations grows as a large epiphytic tree. Another undescribed species with smaller, rounder leaves grows on the rocky ridges at Bajo del Tigre. *Tovomitopsis* spp. are free-standing small trees with white latex. Other *Clusia* species have white, pale yellow or clear latex.

Comments. The yellow latex of some *Clusia* species is used in folk medicine and as a glue, e.g., "an energetic purgative, for healing wounds, for patching boots, and making a pectoral tea" (Pittier 1978). Several individuals are cultivated at the Hotel de Montaña. All species are dioecious. The flowers of *C. stenophylla* open at night and produce a strong, pleasant fragrance that attracts moths; hummingbirds and butterflies clean up the residual nectar in the morning. Birds eat the arillate seeds. The star-shaped dehisced capsules are often found along forest trails.

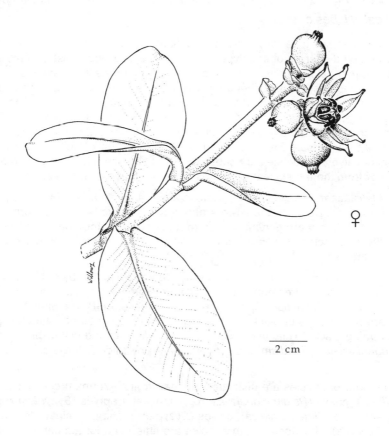

♀

2 cm

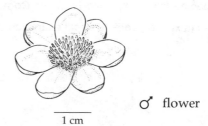

♂ flower

1 cm

MYRTACEAE—Myrtle and Eucalyptus family

Field characters: *simple opposite entire leaves with translucent dots, aromatic odor, flower with inferior ovary and numerous stamens, fruit with persistent calyx lobes or scar at tip.*

The Myrtaceae is a large, worldwide family of trees and some shrubs. Except for some species of eucalyptus with alternate leaves, most species are fairly uniform in having simple, opposite leaves without teeth, mostly glabrous, and with characteristic translucent dots (visible against a strong light). The flowers have an inferior ovary, 4–5 small, free sepals and petals, numerous stamens forming a brush-like mass, and a single exserted style with a minute stigma. The fruits in our area are mostly fleshy drupes (with 1–2 seeds), although *Psidium* (guava) has numerous small seeds. The Southeast Asia/Pacific group that includes eucalyptus produces dry capsules. Most species release a strong aromatic odor from the translucent oil glands when the leaves are shredded.

The Myrtaceae is an important group in most tropical forests, but especially at mid-elevations. Because the flowers and leaves tend to be very uniform, the species of this family are generally easy to recognize to family, but very difficult to identify to species. The fruits provide the best characters for separating closely related species.

The flowers of most Costa Rican Myrtaceae are pollinated by bees. In other regions of the world, birds and nectar-feeding mammals may be pollinators. As in many groups with animal-dispersed fruits, the smaller ones are eaten by birds (these are red, orange or black and often go through a series of color changes before turning black), while the larger ones with more muted yellow-brown colors (*Eugenia valerii, Psidium guajava*) are eaten by mid- to large-sized mammals.

A number of species are cultivated for their fruits—Surinam cherry (*Eugenia uniflora*), guava (*Psidium guajava*), rose and water apples (*Syzygium* spp.), spices—allspice *(Pimenta dioica)*, cloves (*Syzygium*), and medicinal oils (*Eucalyptus, Pimenta*). The Costa Rican species are little used for lumber, but eucalyptus is important in Australia and has been planted extensively in Costa Rica.

Species Diversity—World: 3850; **Costa Rica:** 62; **Monteverde:** 29

See next two pages for local examples of **Myrtaceae**.

Eugenia guatemalensis — *Murta blanco, Multa*
Myrtaceae – Myrtle and Eucalyptus family

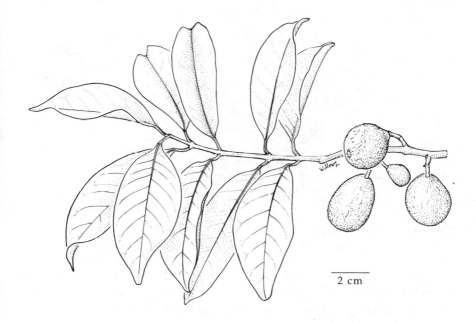

2 cm

Description. A medium-sized tree (8–25 m); LEAVES to 4 x 8 cm, elliptic, somewhat leathery, glabrous, translucent yellow oil glands; shredded leaves have an aromatic odor; FLOWERS white, 1 cm, with 4 small petals and many stamens forming a brush-like ball, fragrant; FRUITS 2.5 cm, brown and hard when immature, becoming yellow and soft when mature, with a surface like leather; 1–2 smooth, off-round, light brown seeds.

Habitat and Phenology. Common in forest, old fields, and edge from 1300–1550 m. FL: JUL–OCT; FR: APR–JUL, OCT–NOV.

Similar species. The thick, glossy, dark leaves with paler undersides are distinctive. *E. octopleura* has smaller leaves with long petioles and smooth, oblong fruit that change from red to black. In most species of *Eugenia*, the fruits are more distinctive than the flowers or leaves, making identification to species extremely difficult.

Comments. This is the most abundant member of the family around the Monteverde community and lower Preserve. The flowers produce pollen as the only reward to pollinators, mostly stingless bees (*Melipona*). The fruits are eaten by bats and less commonly by emerald toucanets (Carlos Guindon, pers. comm.).

97

Myrcianthes fragrans — Albajaquillo
Myrtaceae – Myrtle and Eucalyptus family — Calico tree

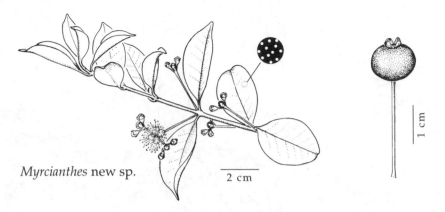

Myrcianthes new sp.

2 cm

1 cm

Description. A medium to large canopy tree (15–30 m); TRUNK often buttressed, bark smooth and peeling in small flakes leaving a chipped calico pattern of red, brown and gray; LEAVES to 3 x 5 cm, elliptic with a blunt tip, leathery, glabrous, translucent yellow oil glands, a faint aromatic odor; FLOWERS white, 7 mm, 4 small rounded petals and numerous stamens forming a ball, strong sweet fragrance; FRUIT an 8 mm juicy red berry with 1–2 soft yellow-green seeds.

Habitat and Phenology. Occasional in mature forest, especially on ridges, and often left as a pasture remnant, at 1300–1500 m. FL: APR–JUL, SEP–OCT; FR: DEC–JAN.

Similar species. A very similar species (not yet named) with rough, cinnamon colored bark and black fruit is common at slightly lower elevations (1200–1450 m), e.g., Bajo del Tigre (see illustration). This black-fruited species has a much stronger leaf odor than *M. fragrans*. *Psidium guajava* (guava), with similar smooth bark, is an abundant treelet in pastures. Two other species of Myrtaceae (*Calyptranthes* spp.), found on high, cloud forest ridges also have smooth, peeling bark.

Comments. The pale, calico trunk is recognizable from a distance. The extremely hard, red wood dulls saw blades, so trees are often left standing when pastures are cleared. The fragrant flowers attract bees, which visit the flowers to collect pollen. No nectar is produced. Holding a leaf up to the light, one can see tiny translucent dots (a hand lens is helpful). These are glands that store the aromatic oils that give Myrtaceae their characteristic piny odor. These chemicals protect the leaves from herbivorous insects that have not evolved specific chemical systems for detoxifying these oils. The wood is valued as firewood for cooking.

98

Pisonia sylvatica
Nyctaginaceae – Four-o'clock family

Description. An understory treelet (2–5 m); 1 cm SPINES arising from the leaf axils and opposite twig junctions; LEAVES to 4 x 8 cm, oval, with one leaf at a node 2–4 times larger than the other; dioecious; small cream FLOWERS in pendulous round heads; FRUIT 1 cm long, elliptic, dry, brown and indehiscent, the surface with several lines of sticky glands.

Habitat and Phenology. Occasional to locally common in the understory of mature forest at 1250–1450 m. FL: sporadic; FEB–MAR, SEP, NOV; FR: MAR.

Similar species. The unequal leaves are distinctive. This is also one of the few spiny plants in forests of the region, although a few species of spiny *Solanum* and *Randia* occur in the area. *Pisonia aculeata* is a rare, canopy liana found on the drier Pacific slope with similar leaves and heavy, recurved thorns.

Comments. This species of *Pisonia* is known only from the Cordillera de Tilarán. The moth-pollinated flowers are fragrant at night. The entire fruiting cluster tends to come off the plant as a unit when the sticky fruits cling to passing birds and mammals, and this is presumably the method of seed dispersal.

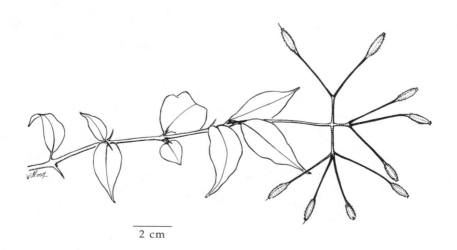

2 cm

99

Salacia petenensis
Hippocrateaceae – Hippocratea family

Siete cueros

"Seven skins"

Description. A subcanopy tree (5–20 m); LEAVES to 7 x 16 cm, elliptic, without teeth, thick and leathery, very dark green above, glabrous; pale green buds, tiny rust-brown, bell-shaped FLOWERS crowded in dense, much-branched inflorescences along the twigs and branches, producing a strong, unpleasant odor like spoiled fruit; FRUIT a 5–8 cm ball with a tough brown rind, containing 3–6 large oblong seeds imbedded in a sweet, jelly-like matrix.

Habitat and Phenology. Rare, found in mature forest, especially on cloud forest ridges exposed to wind-driven mist (1500–1700 m); also on the Atlantic slope. FL: MAR–MAY, OCT–NOV; FR: NOV–JUN.

Similar species. Another *Salacia* species, a large canopy liana with similar fruits and leaves, is more common in Monteverde than the tree. The large leaves and fruit make this tree superficially similar to *Persea americana*, *Pouteria fossicola*, and *Randia matudae*.

Comments. The leathery skinned fruits do not open, but produce a strong, sickish-sweet, fruity odor for many days while still on the tree. This odor presumably attracts monkeys and other arboreal mammals that serve as seed dispersers. Only a small percentage of people seem to find the fruit odor pervasive. The fruits are said to be especially attractive to kinkajous. In cross-section, the wood has distinct thick rings; the local name refers to the wood layers that separate into canoe-like shells upon drying.

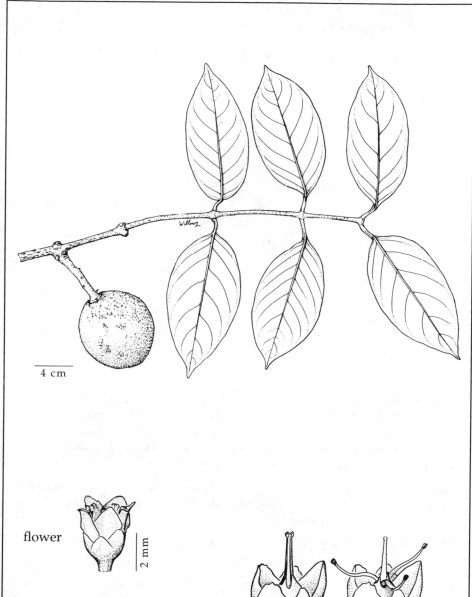

4 cm

flower

2 mm

flower with corolla removed, showing ♂ ♀ phases

1 mm

Symphonia globulifera   *Cerillo*
Clusiaceae – Mangosteen family   Peppermint candy tree

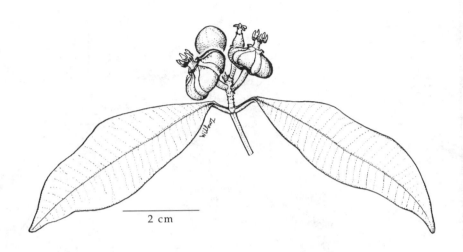

2 cm

Description. A small to medium tree (4–12 m); bark almost black, LATEX bright yellow; LEAVES to 4 x 10 cm, elliptic, glabrous, the secondary veins obscure; the deep pink buds are round, the FLOWERS are squashed globes with 5 pink and white petals and a protuberant red style and staminal column; FRUIT a 2.5 cm oblong yellow-green drupe.

Habitat and Phenology. Uncommon, usually in open understory and old light gaps of mature forest or forest edge at 1200–1500 m; also on the Atlantic slope. FL: MAY–OCT (most of year); FR: APR–DEC.

Similar species. In fruit, *Symphonia* could be confused with species of Myrtaceae and Rubiaceae until one discovers the bright yellow latex.

Comments. This is an attractive tree when flowering, although there are rarely many flowers open at one time. Individual trees flower for an extended period of several months or more. The open flowers, which look like peppermint candies, secrete copious nectar and attract hummingbirds as pollinators. Our tree may be a distinct species from the lowland canopy tree with red flowers found commonly in southwestern Costa Rica. As described by Allen (1956) that species has "a small brown, ovoid, fleshy, 1-seeded edible berry."

CLUSIACEAE (GUTTIFERAE)—Mangosteen and Garcinia family

Field characters: *the commonest genus, Clusia, has rubbery, opposite entire leaves, yellow, white or clear latex, and grows as a woody hemi-epiphyte; others are trees with white or orange latex and fleshy opposite leaves with obscure secondary and tertiary veins; fruits of most are dehiscent, star-shaped capsules with arillate seeds; a few are drupes.*

The Clusiaceae consists of treelets to canopy trees and large, woody hemi-epiphytes (*Clusia*). They have simple, opposite, fleshy leaves without teeth, with numerous parallel, but rather obscure, secondary veins, and yellow or orange (sometimes cloudy white or clear) latex; without stipules, but with the terminal pair of hollowed-out petioles pressed together over the terminal bud hidden between their bases. The thick leaves, latex, and hemi-epiphytic habit combine to create a fig-like appearance; however, all figs have alternate leaves.

Most species are dioecious with inflorescences of small to medium-sized white flowers with free petals, prominent stigmas and numerous stamens. While bees are major pollinators, a few species of *Clusia* have nocturnally fragrant flowers that attract moths. Hummingbirds visit *Symphonia* flowers, which are hermaphroditic. Fruits in this family are fleshy drupes eaten by mammals (*Garcinia, Symphonia*) or dehiscent capsules with rubbery valves and arillate seeds dispersed by birds (*Clusia, Tovomitopsis*).

The family has a tropical worldwide distribution (though many *Hypericum* species occur in temperate areas). The genus *Garcinia* includes the mangosteen and a number of other fruit trees in southeast Asia and the source of the watercolor pigment gamboge. *Clusia uvifera* is the autograph tree of tropical beaches. *Calophyllum brasiliense*, cedro María, is an important wood tree of Costa Rica. The main genera at Monteverde include *Clusia* (tree-sized hemi-epiphytes), *Garcinia* (trees with orange drupes), *Symphonia* (pink and white flowers and green drupes), *Tovomitopsis* (small trees with white latex), and *Vismia* (small trees with orange latex and many-seeded berries).

Species Diversity—World: 1350; **Costa Rica:** 63; **Monteverde:** 21

See page listings under **Clusiaceae** in index for local examples.

Clusia capsule

Tabernaemontana longipes   *Cojón, Cachitos, Huevos de chancho*

Apocynaceae – Dogbane family   Dutchman's shoes

Description. A treelet (2–7 m); all parts with copious white latex; LEAVES to 5 x 13 cm, oval, glabrous; FLOWERS pinwheel-shaped, with a 1.5 cm tube and corolla 2 cm across, the 5 lobes white with beige tips, more fragrant at night than during the day; FRUIT a pair of pendant yellow-green pods, 2 x 4 cm, that dehisce along a ventral line, exposing a dangling seed mass covered with bright red-orange arillate tissue.

Habitat and Phenology. Common in forest understory and edge at 1300–1500 m. FL: FEB–AUG (peak APR–JUL); FR: JAN–NOV (sporadic and somewhat variable within populations).

Similar species. *Stemmadenia litoralis* with 8 cm, white trumpet-shaped flowers and similar, but larger fruit, is found below 1400 m. It is rare in Monteverde, but locally common in moist ravines on the Pacific slope at 900–1200 m. *Stemmadenia donnell-smithii*, in the San Luis Valley, has orange flowers.

Comments. Even though the flowers appear to be adapted for pollination by nocturnal moths, we have observed few visitors going to them. Long-tailed manakins eat the arillate seeds. This tree, like its relatives the frangipani and oleander, has copious, white latex that may be poisonous and is said to have medicinal value. It contains some of the same anti-cancer alkaloids found in the rosy periwinkle.

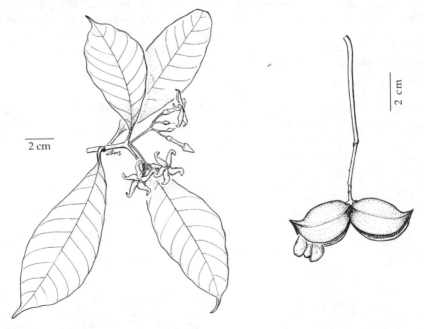

104

Viburnum costaricanum
Caprifoliaceae – Honeysuckle family

Paraviento
"Wind breaker"

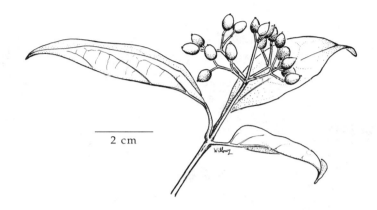

2 cm

Description. A small to medium tree (3–12 m); TRUNK deeply and irregularly fluted; LEAVES to 4 x 8 cm, mostly whorled (3 leaves per node), widest at the middle, often with 2–4 inconspicuous tooth-like glands, glabrous; tiny deciduous STIPULES; small white FLOWERS with 5 lobes (5 mm across), congested in upright, flat-topped clusters at the twig tips, very fragrant; FRUIT an 8 mm shiny black berry with 1 seed.

Habitat and Phenology. Common in secondary forest and edge at 1200–1500 m. FL: MAR–JUN; FR: AUG–NOV.

Similar species. Two other *Viburnum* species, both with opposite leaves, occur here: *V. stellatotomentosum*, with round, wooly pubescent leaves, grows on the dry slopes at 1100–1300 m (common at Bajo del Tigre and Hotel de Montaña); and *V. venustum*, with round, glabrous leaves grows on peaks and ridges along the Continental Divide. *Cornus disciflora* has opposite leaves of similar size, but they are light green with prominent veins.

Comments. The leaves have one or two pairs of nectar glands along the leaf margin near the base. This species is pollinated by stingless bees (*Trigona* spp.). The fruits are eaten by at least eight species of birds. This tree has potential for use in windbreaks and as living fences. The Spanish name literally means "stop wind." The soft, white wood turns rust-red on exposure to the air. The development of marginal teeth is somewhat variable, but they are usually weak or absent in *V. costaricanum*, and more evident in the other species.

105

GROUP 7.
LEAVES ALTERNATE,
VENATION PALMATE

Croton monteverdensis

3 cm

Croton monteverdensis *Targuá*

Euphorbiaceae – Spurge and Poinsettia family   Popcorn tree

Description. A small to medium tree (5–25 m); LEAVES to 9 x 17 cm, oval with a round to faintly lobed base, long petioles, dentate, membranous and scratchy to the touch (with tiny star-shaped, scale-like hairs), a pair of stalked nectar glands near the tip of the petiole, clear sap; small green FLOWERS with beige pubescence; FRUIT a 1 cm brown capsule with 3 seeds.

Habitat and Phenology. A common successional tree in old pastures and secondary forest at 1300–1500 m, occasionally becoming a canopy tree in mature forest, typically growing in light gaps. FL: MAY–AUG; FR: NOV–DEC.

Similar species. *Croton draco* with larger leaves and scarlet sap grows at lower elevations on the Pacific slope (700–1400 m). Dying leaves of both species tend to turn bright orange before they fall. Two other species (*C. watsonii* and *C. xalapensis*) occur in the Río Guacimal valley. *Croton niveus* with larger, spiny fruits is planted in local windbreaks.

Comments. Most Euphorbiaceae have 3-branched stigmas and 3-lobed fruits, and some species exude poisonous, white latex. This species is usually found with flowers of one sex on a given tree (dioecy), but flowers of both sexes can sometimes be found on the same individual (monoecy). Fruits of this species are explosive; on warm days in November and December the fruits open with a loud pop, shooting the seeds out in all directions. This is another of the common pasture trees like *Trema*, *Cecropia*, and *Humpeu* that grow rapidly in high light conditions. *Croton* species have been used in folk medicine. The Targuá is said to have value in treating ulcers, while Colpachí (*Croton niveus*) is used to treat diarrhea.

107

Hampea appendiculata *Burío macho, Burío colorado*
Malvaceae – Mallow and Hibiscus family Doll's eyes

Description. A medium to large tree (8–25 m); LEAVES to 10 x 15 cm, the basal pair of secondary veins prominent, each vein with a single nectar gland below near the middle, the blade underside with dense, rusty-beige pubescence; dioecious; 1–3 FLOWERS per leaf axil, 1.5 cm, with 5 yellow petals and many bright yellow stamens; FRUIT a 2–3 cm brown capsule that opens with 3 valves, to expose 3–6 black seeds half covered by white arils.

Habitat and Phenology. Common in old pastures and secondary forest, also becoming a canopy tree in light gaps of primary forest (900–1600 m); also on the Atlantic slope. FL: MAY–AUG; FR: FEB–MAY.

Similar species. Although the beige leaf underside and nectaries make this species unique, saplings can be confused with those of *Croton* and *Heliocarpus*. The smooth bark has transverse cracks like stitches. *Heliocarpus* has similar small flaps at the leaf base, but the leaves often have a pair of lobes; *Croton* has a pair of extrafloral nectaries on the petiole and stellate hairs.

Comments. *Melipona* bees pollinate the flowers, which also attract many butterflies. The fruits attract over 20 species of birds as well as white-faced monkeys. The trunk sounds hollow when tapped. The wood is soft like balsa, and is used for making forming boards and bed slats. Cut bark secretes a watery sap containing yellow particles. The bark is so tough and fibrous that it can push out nails. Fibers from the bark serve as a twine substitute.

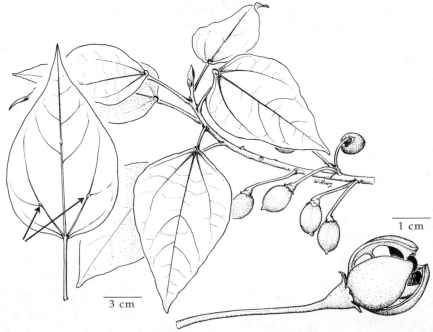

108

Hasseltia floribunda   *Layo, Raspa lengua, Muñeca*

Flacourtiaceae – Flacourtia family

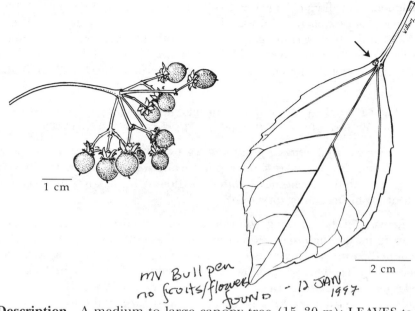

1 cm

2 cm

mv Bull pen
no fruits/flowers
found - 12 JAN 1997

Description. A medium to large canopy tree (15–30 m); LEAVES to 6 x 13 cm, widest beyond the middle and gradually narrowing to the base, a pair of round nectar glands at the base of the blade on the upper side, margin toothed, glabrous; small white FLOWERS with 30–40 stamens, bright orange nectar disk at base of ovary; FRUIT a round red to maroon 1 cm berry, with prominent 4 to 5-lobed calyx at base, 2–4 smooth green seeds.

Habitat and Phenology. Common in mature forest and edge at 1400–1550 m. FL: somewhat sporadic with peak in JAN–FEB; FR: APR–MAY.

Similar species. *Hasseltiopsis dioica* (with larger, black berries), *Macrohasseltia macroterantha* (with wind-dispersed seeds), and *Xylosma* spp. (with branched spines on the trunk) have similar leaves, but they lack the nectar glands at the base of the leaf blade that identify *Hasseltia*.

Comments. This is an abundant tree in our area with distinctive leaves—a leaf picked up from the ground can identify the species. The flowers are pollinated by small bees, such as *Trigona* and *Melipona*. The fruits are conspicuous and attract at least 14 species of birds. They have a delicious flavor and have been used locally for making jam. The trees have been confused with *Macrohasseltia* by wood cutters; however, the poor quality wood of *Hasseltia* rots rapidly, while that of *Macrohasseltia* is durable.

109

Heliocarpus americanus *Burío*

Tiliaceae – Basswood and Linden family

Description. A medium to large tree (5–25 m); large oval LEAVES to 24 x 20 cm with long petioles swollen at the apex, leaf blade pubescent, a pair of small, ear-like lobes at the base, serrate margin with or without a pair of pointed lobes; dioecious; 1 cm yellow FLOWERS with 5 narrow petals; 1 cm, pink to maroon dry FRUIT with long, hairy rays in a plane; the dense fruit clusters held above the leaves.

Habitat and Phenology. Common in primary forest light gaps, old pastures, and secondary forest from 1400–1550 m. FL: AUG–NOV; FR: DEC–FEB.

Similar species. *Heliocarpus appendiculatus* grows lower on the Pacific slope at 1100–1300 m. The leaves are similar to those of *H. americanus*, but the flowers are smaller, and the phenology is different (flowers from November to January; fruits from December to March).

Comments. This fast-growing, soft-wooded tree colonizes landslides, eroded river margins, and light gaps in mature forest, as well as readily taking over abandoned pastures. These trees are conspicuous from as far away as a kilometer with either their pale yellow flowers or dull red fruits. The balsa-like wood is used for building crates for air-shipping delicate fruit. The mucilaginous secretion from the bark is used in local sugar making to lighten the sugar and clean out particulate debris.

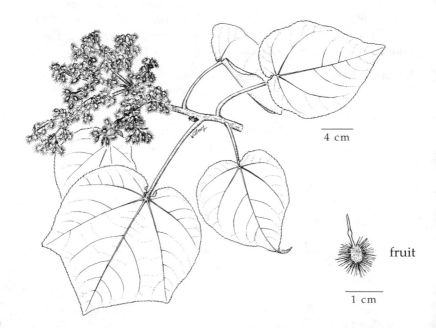

4 cm

fruit

1 cm

110

Malvaviscus palmanus

Amapola, Quesito

Malvaceae – Mallow and Hibiscus family

Turk's cap

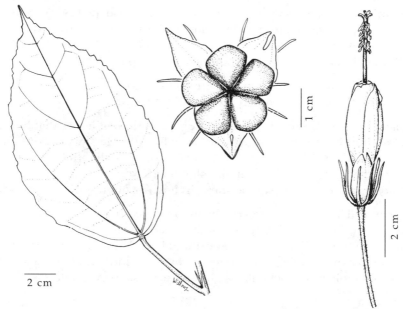

Description. A small tree (2–5 m); LEAVES to 12 x 20 cm, oval with strongly ascending basal veins, margin with large blunt teeth; conspicuous lance-shaped STIPULES; 5 cm red FLOWERS with 5 petals overlapping in a pin-wheel pattern; 2 cm FRUIT with 5 separate spongy lobes changing from white when immature to red-orange when mature.

Habitat and Phenology. Common in open understory, light gaps, forest edges and roadsides at 1500–1600 m, and rare in moist ravines at lower elevations. FL: most of the year, but more exuberant during wet season; FR: all year.

Similar species. A second species, *M. arboreus*, occurs below 1400 m on the Pacific and Atlantic slopes. It is distinct in having a broader, maple-shaped leaf and the cells of the fruit are fused together, not lobed. While *M. palmanus* always grows as a shrub or small tree, the growth form of *M. arboreus* varies from a shrub in high light situations to a scrambling liana that can reach the canopy in primary forest.

Comments. The large, red flowers are pollinated by hummingbirds, but *Heliconius* and clear-winged ithomiid butterflies also visit them occasionally. The fruits are eaten by prong-billed barbets and emerald toucanets. Stripped pieces of the bark can be used as string.

111

Piper auritum   *Estrella*

Piperaceae – Black pepper family

Description. A small weedy tree (3–6 m); large heart-shaped LEAVES to 30 x 40 cm, soft pubescent and membranous with a strong sassafras odor when shredded; minute white FLOWERS on erect thin spikes to 25 cm long; FRUITS on thicker gray green pendulous spikes up to 30 cm long.

Habitat and Phenology. Common in second growth and edge habitats throughout the area. FL and FR throughout the year.

Similar species. *Piper imperiale* with stiffer, heart-shaped leaves that lack the sassafras odor occurs in light gaps and open forest understory above 1550 m and on the Atlantic slope. Many other species of *Piper*, all with smaller leaves, occur in the area. They have similar slender flowering and fruiting spikes, and most have prominent stipule scars circling the often swollen leaf nodes.

Comments. The fragrant leaves can be used to make a very nice substitute for sassafras tea; however, it is not recommended because the leaves contain safrole, a phenolic oil that causes cancer and liver damage. Along with many other species of *Piper*, the fruits are eaten by bats. Little is known about the pollination biology of pipers, although some are visited by stingless bees (*Trigona* spp.).

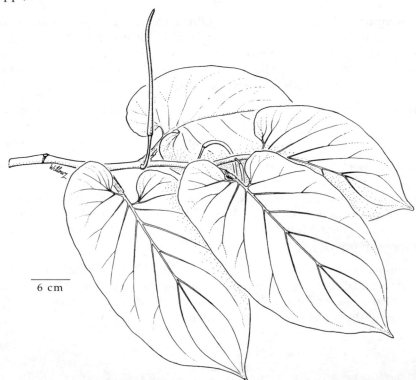

6 cm

112

Trema micrantha *Capulín*
Ulmaceae – Elm family

Description. A medium-sized tree (5–20 m); LEAVES to 5 x 12 cm, lance-shaped with a lobed base, the basal secondary veins strongly ascending, margin finely serrate, the upper side rough; FLOWERS cream-white, small and inconspicuous on short, axillary inflorescences; FRUIT a 3 mm orange berry with 1 green seed, clustered along twigs among or below the leaves.

Habitat and Phenology. Common in pastures and roadsides, secondary forest, and in large light gaps in mature forest at 1200–1550 m. FL: any month, peak in JAN–APR; FR: MAY–SEP.

Similar species. *Casearia tacanensis* has similarly shaped leaves also held in a plane, but the venation is pinnate, and the flowers and fruit are distinct. *Perrottetia longistylis,* with a similar growth form and dense clusters of tiny red berries, is common in light gaps and forest edges above 1500 m.

Comments. Because this tree can colonize bare road banks and overgrazed and degraded land, it has potential for erosion control and habitat restoration. The reduced flowers appear wind-pollinated, but we have heard that they are sometimes visited by insects. The fruits attract at least 16 bird species. The trunks often have deep holes covered by a cap of sawdust and debris held together with silk. These are made by caterpillars of a large moth (Hepialidae), which emerges in April—just a few days after the first heavy showers. The wood, relatively hard for a fast-growing species, can be used for beams if it is kept dry. While people in San Luis have some medicinal uses for the fibrous bark, a more widespread use is as a string substitute.

113

Urera elata *Ortiga*

Urticaceae – Nettle family Stinging nettle

Description. A shrub to small tree (2–6 m); LEAVES large (to 20 x 30 cm), oval with a rounded base, margin toothed, petiole and midvein pink to red, sparsely pubescent to glabrous; dioecious; FLOWERS in tightly congested inflorescences along the branches, sometimes with urticating hairs, the male flowers pink, the females light green; tiny, bright orange, one-seeded FRUIT in dense clusters along the stems and branches.

Habitat and Phenology. Common in secondary forest, light gaps in mature forest, and forest edges above 1500 m. FL: FEB–APR, NOV–DEC; FR: NOV–APR.

Similar species. Another common species here at 1200–1500 m is *U. caracasana* with pubescent, heart-shaped leaves with a pimply surface texture. A less common species with narrower elliptic leaves occurs in river canyons on the Pacific slope. Two *Myriocarpa* species also found here are vegetatively similar to the ureras, but they have long, dangling, thread-like inflorescences with tiny dry fruits, and they do not have stinging hairs.

Comments. In our area this species has few urticating hairs, and these are most likely to occur on the inflorescences; this and other species tend to be more urticating in the lowlands. The plants are wind-pollinated; the anthers pop open to release tiny clouds of pollen on sunny mornings. *Urera* fruits are eaten by some 13 species of birds.

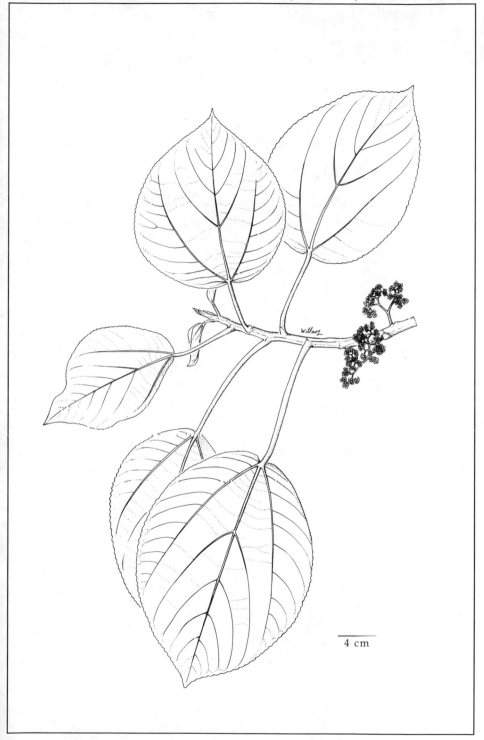

4 cm

GROUP 8.
LEAVES ALTERNATE, VENATION PINNATE,
LEAF MARGIN TOOTHED

Bocconia frutescens   *Guacamayo*
Papaveraceae – Poppy family

Description. A shrubby treelet to small tree (2–10 m); LEAVES to 15 x 40 cm, but highly variable, deeply lobed and also serrate, widening toward the tip with a gradually narrowed base, glabrous, pale gray-green below; monoecious; large unisexual inflorescences (10–40 cm) with numerous pale FLOWERS lacking petals; 1 cm elliptic, tan FRUITS with a persisting forked style, opening by two valves that fall away to expose a single black seed with bright red aril.

Habitat and Phenology. Common on roadsides, cut banks, and in old pastures and second growth as well as in large light gaps in primary forest from 1300–1700 m, though more abundant above 1500 m. FL: most of year; FR: most abundant from MAR–MAY.

Similar species. *Senecio cooperi* and *Senecio copeyensis* (Asteraceae) have a similar growth form and lobed leaves, but their large yellow flowers distinguish them from *Bocconia*.

Comments. This is a very common weedy treelet of roadsides and secondary habitats that rarely becomes tree-sized with a 20 cm trunk. Large individuals develop a tan, fissured bark similar to that of *Acnistus*. The cut twigs ooze a watery, orange sap that lightly stains the skin (the sap is more evident in the roots). This sap is used on warts, while a caustic oil in the seeds is used to kill external parasites. The manner in which the fruits dehisce is worth a close look. The seeds are eaten by long-tailed manakins and elaenia flycatchers.

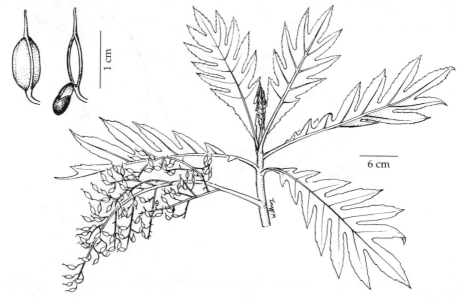

117

FLACOURTIACEAE—Flacourtia family

Field characters: *simple alternate leaves with either pinnate or palmate venation, often with teeth, often 2-ranked, with deciduous stipules, flowers often with numerous stamens.*

One could describe this as a catch-all family. The flacourts are generally rather nondescript trees or shrubs with simple, alternate, often serrate leaves either spiraling or in a plane, and with deciduous stipules. Some species have prominent stipules, spines, nectar glands at the base of the leaf blade, 3-veined leaves or translucent dots. Branching spines on the trunk of *Xylosma* (see illus.) are conspicuous. The flowers, usually in axillary inflorescences, are small and whitish with numerous stamens. The fruits of our species are either dehiscing 3-lobed capsules with arillate seeds (e.g., *Casearia*) or fleshy berries (e.g., *Hasseltia*)—both with seeds dispersed by birds. However, one exception is *Casearia tacanensis*, which produces a large, indehiscent capsule with a rubbery rind containing a gooey mass of small seeds that attracts arboreal mammals (see text). Another exception (*Macrohasseltia*) has hairy seeds that float in the wind.

The flacourts are mostly tropical and subtropical in distribution. They have minor uses as timber, medicinal oils for the treatment of leprosy, edible fruits, and as ornamentals. Though inconspicuous, the flacourts make up a significant percentage of the species in most Costa Rican forests.

Species Diversity—World: 875; **Costa Rica:** 47; **Monteverde:** 21

See page listings under **Flacourtiaceae** in index for local examples.

Xylosma trunk

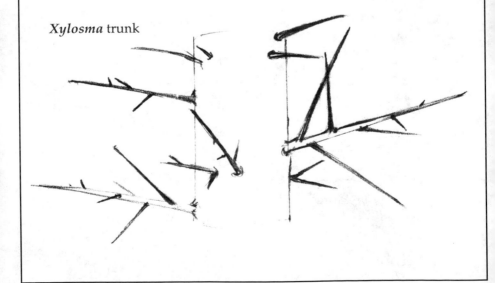

118

Casearia tacanensis

Flacourtiaceae – Flacourtia family

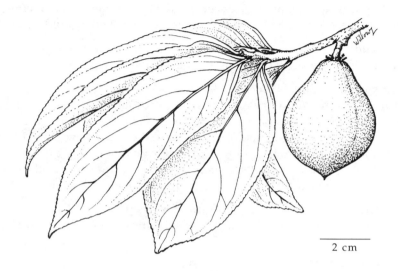

2 cm

Description. A subcanopy tree (8–20 m); LEAVES to 5 x 14 cm, held in a plane, elliptic with a saw-toothed margin, glabrous; small pale green FLOWERS with 5 narrow petals, forming dense clusters in leaf axils, producing a strong honey-like fragrance; FRUIT a leathery, yellow-green 3–5 cm long, indehiscent teardrop-shaped capsule with 3 valves, a jam-like orange mass of seeds and juicy arils inside, with a strong odor similar to passion fruit.

Habitat and Phenology. Common in mature forest at 1300–1600 m. FL: flowering extends over several months, peak in JAN–FEB; FR: APR–JUL.

Similar species. *Casearia sylvestris* has smaller leaves, and flowers with 1 cm fruits that open to offer red arillate seeds. *Perrottetia longistylis* at higher elevations has similar leaves, but the flowers and fruits are much smaller.

Comments. Although one of the commonest subcanopy trees in the upper community to lower Preserve, *Casearia* is inconspicuous unless observed while flowering or fruiting. The odorous fruits accumulate under the tree as they are torn open and scattered by arboreal mammals. Although the fruits have three valves like other species of *Casearia*, they never seem to open (dehisce) by themselves .

119

Clethra lanata   Nance macho
Clethraceae – Pepperbush family

Description. A small to medium tree (3–15 m) with low, open crown; LEAVES to 5 x 12 cm, bunched at twig tips, widest beyond middle, dense carpet of beige pubescence on underside, teeth faint or absent; 5 mm FLOWERS with 5 white petals and 10 orange brown anthers, spaced along 10–20 spikes at the twig tips, a pungent lily-like scent; FRUIT a 7 mm capsule opening by 3 valves, numerous minute flat brown seeds are dispersed by wind.

Habitat and Phenology. Common on cut road banks and in old pastures on the dry Pacific slope at 700–1400 m. FL: JAN–MAR; FR: APR–MAY.

Similar species. Another species, *Clethra mexicana* (illustrated) occurs above 1400 m and extends down the Atlantic slope. Although the flowers and fruits are similar to those of *C. lanata*, it has a tall, straight growth form, the cinnamon bark peels in fine longitudinal flakes, and the leaves have more distinct teeth. It flowers from May to July and fruits from September to November. *Clethra* is superficially similar to *Saurauia*, which has branched, axillary inflorescences with large, white flowers and fruits that open in 5 sections.

Comments. *Clethra* has a natural affinity for steep, eroded banks and may have some utility for erosion control on the highly overgrazed Pacific slope.

Meliosma idiopoda
Sabiaceae – Sabia and Snake-seed family   Diamond seed

Description. A subcanopy tree (5–15 m); LEAVES to 5 x 15 cm, spiraled and somewhat bunched at the twig tips, widest beyond the middle, with or without a few sharp teeth near the tip, the petiole base bulbous; tiny white FLOWERS; FRUIT 1 cm, globose, translucent white when mature, with 1 seed.

Habitat and Phenology. Abundant in moist forest from 1200–1500 m, also on the Atlantic slope. FL: FEB–APR; FR: SEP–FEB.

Similar species. Three other species of *Meliosma* overlap with *M. idiopoda*. *M. subcordata* is a rare subcanopy tree of the cloud forest with pubescent, oak-like leaves and 2 cm fruits; *M. vernicosa* (page 133) is a common canopy tree of the cloud forest with 3 cm brown fruits. Leaves of *M. idiopoda* can be confused with those of the oak, *Quercus brenesii*, which has stipules and produces acorns.

Comments. This species can be showy in full flower. The corollas are spring-loaded, so that when the flower is touched by a pollinator (mostly wasps), the corolla pops off and falls away. The fruits never become soft or juicy, do not appear edible, and brown rotted fruits often remain on the tree. However, they are eaten by emerald toucanets and mountain robins when they are white and the rind is crunchy. The gray-brown stone-like seeds have a faceted surface that is hard enough to etch glass.

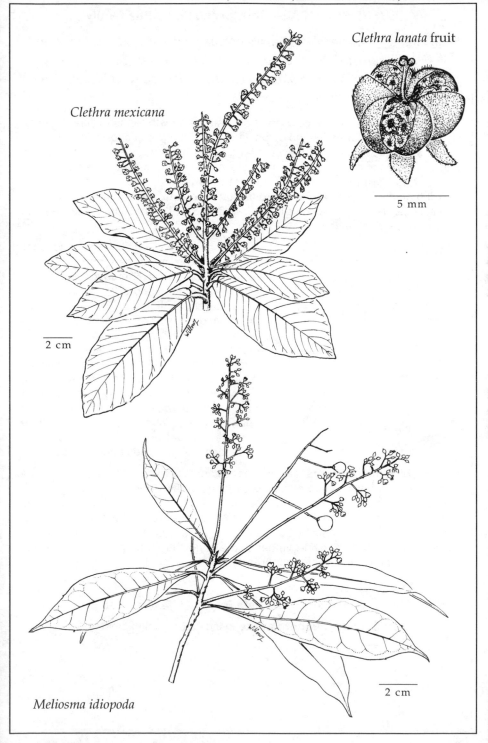

Clethra lanata fruit

5 mm

Clethra mexicana

2 cm

Meliosma idiopoda

2 cm

EUPHORBIACEAE—Spurge and Poinsettia family

Field characters: *a family not easily characterized as a whole, but often with simple alternate leaves, stipules, white or clear sap, scaly or scurfy pubescence, extrafloral nectar glands at the petiole apex, unisexual flowers, and capsules with three lobes.*

This large family includes a great diversity of growth forms including herbs, shrubs, trees and lianas (but no epiphytes) and a number of cactus-like plants in Africa. Most trees and shrubs have alternate leaves and a subset of characters that include white or cloudy latex, palmate leaf venation, stellate or scaly pubescence, a pair of nectar glands at the petiole apex, stipules, unisexual flowers with 3-branched styles and numerous stamens, and dehiscent 3-lobed fruits with persistent stigmas. Species lacking white latex often have toothy leaves and petioles of varying lengths.

Sapium leaf

Euphorbs are either monoecious or dioecious. The more generalized flowers (e.g., *Croton*) have 5 petals and sepals, about 10 stamens and a 3-branched style. More advanced flowers (*Euphorbia*) lack petals and consist of a naked ovary and styles in female flowers and groups of stamens in the male flowers. Insects such as bees, wasps and butterflies pollinate euphorbs. While a few species have fleshy, animal dispersed drupes or berries (*Drypetes*, *Margaritaria*), the majority of our species have 3-lobed capsules that either explode to shoot out the seeds or dehisce to expose arillate seeds that attract birds.

Although the euphorbs are cosmopolitan in distribution, they are more diverse in the tropics. *Manihot esculenta* is one of the world's top ten food crops (cassava, tapioca) and natural rubber comes from the South American tree *Hevea brasiliensis*. The poinsettia (*Euphorbia pulcherrima*) is one of many ornamentals and the castor bean (*Ricinus communis*) produces an oil of commercial value. A few species provide timber and among the many poisonous species are a few that have medicinal properties.

Species Diversity—World: 7950; **Costa Rica:** 177; **Monteverde:** 50

See page listings under **Euphorbiaceae** in index for local examples.

122

Sapium glandulosum *Yos*

Euphorbiaceae – Spurge and Poinsettia family

Description. A medium to large tree (10–30 m); LEAVES to 5 x 9 cm, elliptic, margin faintly toothed or entire, leathery, a pair of 1 mm long, stalked glands at the end of the petiole, glabrous; monoecious; tiny greenish-red FLOWERS without petals on erect spikes; briefly leafless in dry season; FRUIT a 1 cm 3-lobed capsule dehiscing to expose 1–3 black seeds with red arils.

Habitat and Phenology. Common in pastures and occasional in mature forest at 1300–1550 m. FL: MAR–MAY, NOV–DEC; FR: MAY, AUG–NOV.

Similar species. *Sapium rigidifolium* is a large canopy tree of the high cloud forest, found in exposed sites above 1550 m (Pantanoso Trail, Chomogo Trail). It has smaller leaves of a more uniform size than *S. glandulosum. S. laurifolium* (larger leaf without teeth) and *S. macrocarpum* (leaf tips curled like elfin slippers) grow below 1300 m on the Pacific slope. The copious white latex is reminiscent of *Ficus,* which has large stipules.

Comments. The yos is a conspicuous tree in Monteverde pastures. The reduced flowers are unisexual, but both sexes are found on the same inflorescence (the sparser female flowers are grouped near the base of the spike). Wasps are the most common visitors. The fruits dehisce on the tree to display conspicuous black seeds with red arils. Twenty-two species of birds have been observed feeding on the fruits. All parts of the plant exude white latex when damaged. The latex is caustic to the skin and may cause temporary blindness. The latex can be used as a glue.

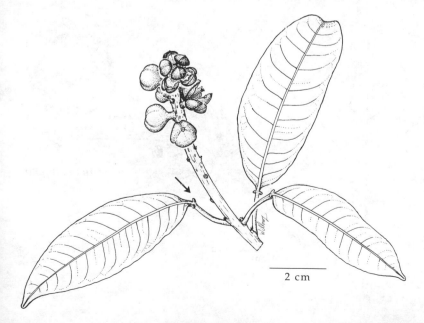

2 cm

123

Saurauia montana *Moco*

Actinidiaceae – Actinidia and Kiwi fruit family "Snot"

Description. A small tree (3–10 m); LEAVES to 8 x 30 cm, spiraled, widest beyond the middle, margin with sharp teeth, rough-pubescent; dioecious; inflorescence with 5–12 flowers; 2 cm FLOWERS with 5 white petals and many orange stamens attached in a ring, the wooly ovary with 5 styles present in female flowers, absent in male; FRUIT a soft, pubescent, green capsule to 2 cm, opening with 5 valves to expose tiny brown seeds imbedded in a slimy, jelly-like matrix.

Habitat and Phenology. Common in old pastures, secondary forest/edge up to 1550 m; also on the Atlantic slope. FL: APR–NOV–FEB (most of year); FR: DEC–FEB.

Similar species. Two other species of *Saurauia* with shorter, broader leaves are found above 1500 m: *S.* "broad leaf" with large erect inflorescences bearing several dozen flowers is common along the road in the Preserve and on the Continental Divide; *S.* "pendant inflo," with drooping inflorescences bearing less than a dozen flowers, is rare and occurs in the high cloud forest on peaks and ridges exposed to the wind-borne mists.

Comments. Pollinated by bees, the flowers produce no nectar, and pollen is the only reward. They also attract beetles, which come to eat the pollen. The female flowers produce sterile pollen that serves as a false reward. The fallen corollas are conspicuous on the ground. The fruits appear to be adapted for dispersal by birds and possibly also by mammals; however, they are not particularly attractive. The fruits are sometimes eaten by local kids. One sometimes finds the jelly-like slime ("moco") and seeds dripping from the open fruits.

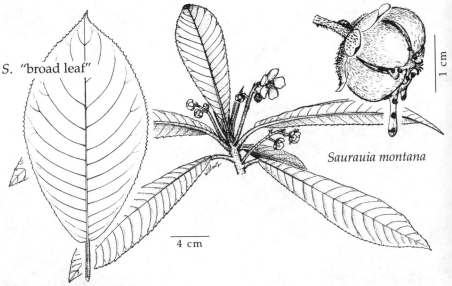

S. "broad leaf"

Saurauia montana

1 cm

4 cm

124

Symplocos limoncillo *Jocotillo*
Symplocaceae – Sweet leaf family

2 cm

Description. A canopy tree (15–25 m); LEAVES to 3.5 x 8 cm, spiraled and bunched at the twig tips, weakly toothed, widest at or just beyond the middle; small white FLOWERS with pink shading in short inflorescences among the leaves; FRUIT a 1.5 cm gray-green drupe with violet flesh and a round scar at the tip.

Habitat and Phenology. Common in primary wet forest and forest edges in the Monteverde community at 1250–1450 m (Bajo del Tigre). FL: MAR–MAY; FR: JUL–OCT.

Similar species. This species can be difficult to distinguish from several others with simple, alternate, toothed leaves. *Symplococarpon purpusii* (Theaceae) overlaps with *S. limoncillo* and has similar leaves, but the flowers are cream-yellow. Species of *Ilex* (Aquifoliaceae) have similar leaves, but the small, white flowers with four petals and stamens and small, round, red fruits distinguish them. Several other species of *Symplocos* also occur in the area, but they are mostly found at higher elevations (above 1450 m).

Comments. The flowers have a pleasant fragrance. They are visited by bees during the day as well as by moths at night. The fruits provide an important food source for quetzals when they move down into the Monteverde community immediately after the breeding season (July–September). The stone-like seeds accumulate under the trees and may then be dispersed by rodents. The seeds can remain viable after years in the soil. The wood is pink when fresh, turning pinkish beige when dry. It is medium hard and has been used in areas above ground that stay dry.

125

Ticodendron incognitum Jaúl macho
Ticodendraceae – Ticodendron family "Male alder"

Description. A subcanopy tree (8–20 m) of old light gaps in primary forest; LEAVES to 7 x 10 cm, held in a plane, glabrous, margin saw-toothed; prominent deciduous STIPULES; dioecious; tiny pink-white male FLOWERS in erect short catkin-like inflorescences in the leaf axils, 1 cm female flowers with forked styles solitary in the leaf axils; FRUIT 3–3.5 cm long, almond-shaped with a tough black rind; SEED almond-shaped with several deep longitudinal grooves, very hard shelled.

Habitat and Phenology. Rare in moist river canyons down to 1400 m on Pacific slope; occasional on exposed peaks and ridges above 1700 m; common on the Atlantic slope at 800–1000 m. FL: FEB–APR; FR: AUG–OCT.

Similar species. *Ticodendron* leaves look much like those of beech and alder of the temperate forest and *Jaúl*, the tropical alder (*Alnus acuminata*)—hence the common name. *Alnus* is cultivated at higher elevations in Costa Rica and grows wild on the Atlantic slope at 700–1200 m. Other local trees with similar foliage include *Casearia tacanensis*, *Perrottetia longistylis* and *Trema micrantha*.

Comments. *Ticodendron* fruits remain green and stay on the tree for months where they attract squirrels. The stone-like, grooved seeds often drop beneath the parent trees where terrestrial rodents chew through the shell to eat the seeds. The hard wood is white when fresh, but soon turns orange on exposure to the air.

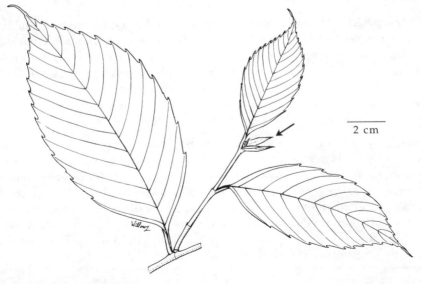

2 cm

126

TICODENDRACEAE—Ticodendron family

Field characters: *simple alternate serrate leaves, solitary almond-sized fruits in leaf axils, blackish dead leaves conspicuous on the ground.*

1 cm

Ticodendron incognitum was described in 1990 as a new species, genus and family. It is the only known representative of its family in the world. It is related to oaks and beeches (Fagaceae) and to alders and birches (Betulaceae). *Ticodendron* was first discovered in Costa Rica in the 1980's, but was later found to occur from southern Mexico to Panama. The leaves turn blackish brown after falling and remain conspicuous on trails. The male flowers are bunched together on short catkins. The greenish female flowers consisting of a naked ovary with two long, forked styles are solitary in the leaf axils. The fruit is a fleshy drupe whose almond-shaped, hard-shelled seed has longitudinal grooves and ridges.

The trees are dioecious with inconspicuous flowers that are presumably wind-pollinated judging from the absence of a showy corolla and because the pollen readily sifts into the air when one taps the branches. The trees flower in March, but only in alternate years. The fruits mature during the following dry season (November–February). The mature fruits are greenish black with a fleshy rind that is presumably attractive to arboreal mammals. We have observed squirrels chewing and dropping large numbers of the immature fruits.

This tree barely reaches the Monteverde community in the deep river ravines descending from the cloud forest. It is more common on the high ridges along the Continental Divide and especially on ridges in the very wet forest on the Atlantic slope.

Species Diversity—World: 1; Costa Rica: 1; Monteverde: 1

Ticodendron seed

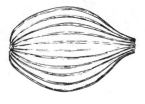

1 cm

127

GROUP 9.
LEAVES ALTERNATE WITHOUT TEETH,
VENATION PINNATE, LEAF BLADE OBOVATE–
DISTINCTLY WIDEST BEYOND THE MIDDLE

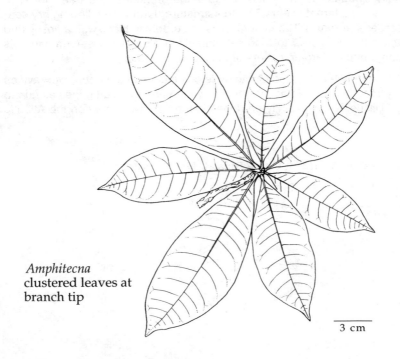

Amphitecna
clustered leaves at
branch tip

3 cm

Amphitecna haberi, sp. nov. ined.
Bignoniaceae – Trumpet creeper family

Jícaro de monte
Cloud forest calabash

Description. A subcanopy tree (8–15 m); LEAVES to 10 x 30 cm, bunched at the twig tips, widest beyond the middle; 3 cm cream-green FLOWERS with a kink in the short tube, malodorous at night; a large green elliptic gourd-like FRUIT with numerous flat seeds embedded in a pulpy matrix.

Habitat and Phenology. Occasional in old light gaps in cloud forest at 1500–1600 m; also on the Atlantic slope. FL: APR, SEP; FR: JUN–AUG, DEC–FEB.

Similar species. A second species, still unidentified and apparently new to science (A. Gentry, pers. comm.), occurs lower on the dry Pacific slope at 1000–1300 m. The leaves and fruits are smaller than *A. haberi,* which is still an unpublished species.

Comments. This tree is inconspicuous until it flowers or fruits. The spent flowers drop to the ground where they are easily noticed. They produce an unpleasant musky odor associated with pollination by nocturnal, nectar-drinking bats. A particular tree rarely has more than a few of these large, green, inconspicuous fruits. They remain on the tree for many months, maturing slowly, then finally fall to the ground where they are presumably eaten by tapirs.

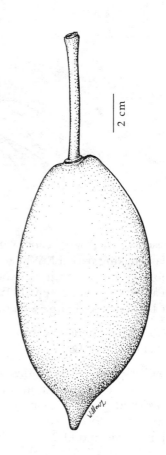

129

Beilschmiedia pendula
Lauraceae – Laurel and Avocado family

Chancho

"Pig"

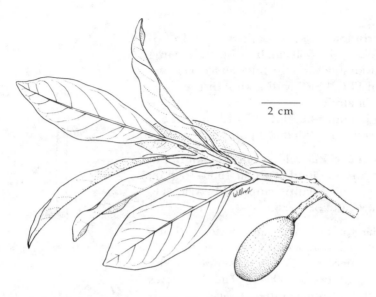

2 cm

Description. A large canopy tree (20–40 m); TRUNK with red-brown, irregularly flaking bark; LEAVES to 4 x 10 cm, spiraled and somewhat bunched at the twig tips, widest just beyond the middle, without teeth, glabrous, odor weak; small yellow-green FLOWERS with 6 tepals; FRUIT a 2.5 x 4–5 cm elliptic black drupe; 1 large seed with rough surface.

Habitat and Phenology. Common in mature forest at 1500–1600 m. FL: MAR–JUN; FR: NOV–MAR.

Similar species. Three other species of *Beilschmiedia* with similar fruits occur at slightly lower elevations on the Pacific slope. *B. brenesii* has small, oval leaves and *B.* cf. *ovalis* has very large rounded leaves. An undescribed species very similar to *B. brenesii* occurs below 1200 m on the Pacific slope between Monteverde and El Dos de Tilarán.

Comments. This is one of the largest trees in the cloud forest, sometimes reaching a meter in diameter. The small, yellowish flowers have six tepals (undifferentiated sepals and petals). The fruits are important in the diet of resplendent quetzals during the nesting season and are also eaten by guans, toucanets, and bellbirds. There is some confusion over which species go with which common names (i.e., chancho, chancho rosado, etc.). The dark, red wood of some *Beilschmiedia* species is valuable, while the white wood of others is of lower quality.

130

Cordia cymosa
Muñeco, Buriogre de altura

Boraginaceae – Borage family

Description. A medium to large canopy tree (10–25 m); LEAVES to 18 x 25 cm, oval to round, often widest beyond the middle, without teeth, thick and leathery, pubescent; dioecious; small white FLOWERS in dense inflorescences held above the foliage; FRUIT a 1 cm white berry.

Habitat and Phenology. Occasional in mature forest and often left in pastures at 1400–1550 m. FL: FEB–APR; FR: SEP–DEC.

Similar species. The large, round to oval pubescent leaves are the best character for this tree. A few other species of *Cordia* with smaller glabrous leaves and orange fruit occur in the area. This species could be mistaken for *Persea schiedeana* at higher elevations or for *Beilschmiedia* cf. *ovalis* and *Ocotea sinuata* below 1500 m, but these trees have much larger fruits.

Comments. *Cordia cymosa* is typically found in old light gaps in mature forest and becomes one of the larger trees in secondary forest. This species is pollinated by small bees. The fruits are eaten by birds. The beige wood has long, elastic fibers and little utility.

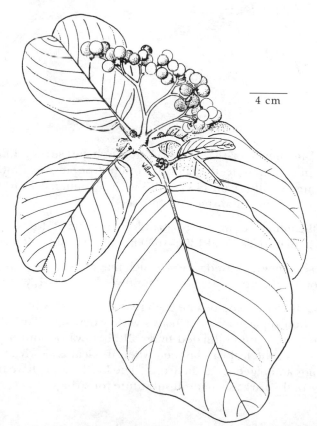

4 cm

131

Daphnopsis americana   *Mastate*

Thymelaeaceae – Mezereum family

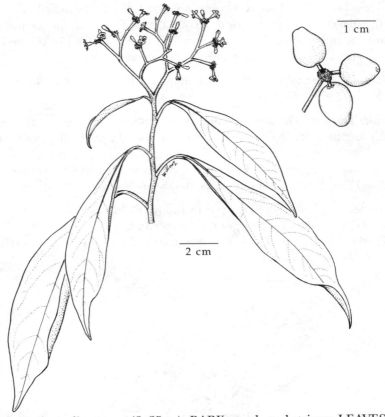

1 cm

2 cm

Description. A medium tree (8–25 m); BARK tough and stringy; LEAVES to 5 x 19 cm, elliptic, without teeth, glabrous, often drooping, leaf with elastic fibers; dioecious; small cream FLOWERS with 4 stamens; 1 cm globose FRUIT cream-white with 1 translucent white seed.

Habitat and Phenology. Common in abandoned pastures, forest edge and old light gaps in mature forest at 1300–1600 m. FL: MAY–JUL; FR: APR–OCT.

Similar species. A smaller leaved variety, which may actually be a distinct species, is common on the dry slopes below Monteverde at 900–1200 m.

Comments. Many trees are defoliated each year in April–May by caterpillars, but the trees soon replace all their leaves with a new set. The plants are dioecious, the flowers are pollinated by small bees, wasps, and butterflies. The elastic fibers in the leaf can be seen when the leaf is slowly torn apart. Mountain robins and pigeons eat the fruits. The local people have traditionally used strips of the bark as a natural substitute for string.

132

Meliosma vernicosa *Espavel de altura*
Sabiaceae – Sabia and Snake-seed family

Description. A canopy tree (20–25 m); large spiraled LEAVES to 10 x 30 cm or more, stiff, widest beyond the middle with a long narrow base, bunched at the twig tips, the petiole base swollen; tiny white FLOWERS in large terminal inflorescences; FRUIT globose, 2.5 cm, green or brown with one seed; SEED stone-like, with a scalloped surface and pointed base.

Habitat and Phenology. Common in the cloud forest from 1500–1700 m, also on the Atlantic slope. FL: JUN–AUG; FR: JAN–JUL.

Similar species. Although they are larger, the leaves of *Meliosma* can be confused with those of the sapote, *Pouteria fossicola.*

Comments. The fruiting trees with large, oblanceolate leaves and terminal fruit clusters are recognizable from a distance. The older leaves often have a transparent appearance after being attacked by skeletonizing moth larvae. The seeds are too hard to cut open and the scalloped surface can etch glass like a diamond. The fruits, which never become soft or bright colored, are presumably eaten by mammals and only rarely by large birds such as quetzals and guans (Nat Wheelwright, pers. comm.). Most individuals are leafless for a month or two in the dry season. The pale pink wood has a fine grain, but because the trunks tend to shatter and split upon falling, they are little used.

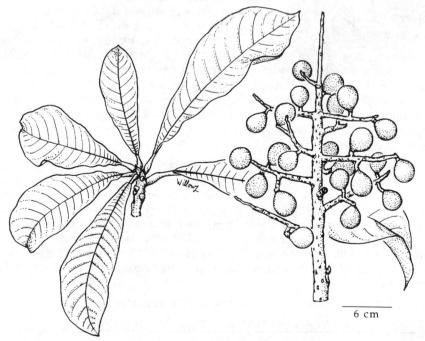

6 cm

133

LAURACEAE—Laurel and Avocado family

Field characters: *simple, alternate, entire leaves arranged spirally, conifer or unripe avocado odor in leaves and bark, small flowers with 6 tepals, and stamens with pollen in pockets with flaps, fruit often with red cupules.*

The Lauraceae is a worldwide family of mostly tropical trees, but with one genus of leafless parasites (*Cassytha*). Most species have rather nondescript simple, alternate leaves. A few species have opposite leaves, though not in our area. The leaves grow in a spiral pattern around the twigs (as opposed to two-ranked in a plane) and always lack teeth and stipules. Leaf shapes are mostly elliptic to obovate with a pointed tip and either glabrous or with a distinctive soft pubescence of simple hairs. The leaves and/or bark always have distinct aromatic odors characteristic of this family (but odor weak in *Beilschmiedia*).

In our area the flowers are fairly uniform in having 6 tepals in two rings and 9 stamens with 2 or 4 distinctive small cavities that contain the pollen. These holes have small membranous flaps that curl upward to make the pollen available to pollinators. The flowers are mostly small (4–8 mm across) and vary from white to pale ˇeen or yellow. The one-seeded fruits have a soft, fleshy rind eaten by large frugivorous birds such as quetzals, bellbirds, and guans, or mammals in the case of some *Persea* species. The fruit stalk of many species expands into a red cup around the base of the black fruit.

flower & anther

The Lauraceae occur in highest abundance and diversity in Costa Rica's cloud forests with the lowest numbers in the lowland dry forest, and intermediate numbers in lowland wet forest habitats. We have collected 66 species in the Monteverde region. A variety of small, mostly generalist pollinators such as flies, wasps, beetles, and butterflies visit the flowers. Most species have round or elliptic seeds within the range of 1 to 3.5 cm long, red cupules and black drupes, and are dispersed by birds. A few species have large round fruits like the avocado that turn yellowish or brownish green when mature. These species attract arboreal mammals such as monkeys and kinkajous. The seed has a papery seed coat that does not protect the seed from drying, so germination occurs soon after dispersal.

The avocado (*Persea americana*) is probably the best-known member of the Lauraceae. It originated in the Neotropics where it was brought into cultivation by indigenous people. The wild progenitor of this fruit occurs naturally in the forests at Monteverde. Old world species of *Cinnamomum* are the source of camphor and cinnamon. In Costa Rica, several genera produce lumber. The wood varies greatly in hardness and durability. A few species produce a deep red hardwood with beautiful grain that has been used for furniture and paneling in our area. Oil of sassafras comes from *Sassafras albidum*, well-known in eastern North America.

Species Diversity— World: 2200; Costa Rica: 120; Monteverde: 66

See page listings under **Lauraceae** in index for local examples.

134

Ocotea tonduzii

Ira marañon

Lauraceae – Laurel and Avocado family

Ira marañon

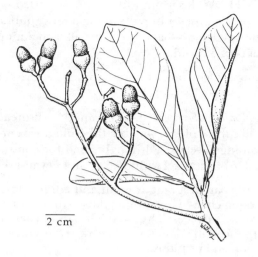

2 cm

Description. A medium to large tree (15–30 m); LEAVES to 8 x 18 cm, spatula-shaped, widest beyond the middle with a blunt tip, thick and leathery, without teeth, the petiole very short and the leaf blade often turned under at the base, nearly glabrous; small yellow FLOWERS that barely open, in large dense inflorescences that stand out beyond the leaves; FRUIT a 1.5 cm black drupe with the receptacle forming a red cupule, held erect; 1 seed.

Habitat and Phenology. Common in mature forest and pastures at 1450–1550 m, also on the Atlantic slope. FL: FEB–AUG, somewhat variable from year to year; FR: OCT–AUG, peak MAR–MAY.

Similar species. A similar, but unnamed species, with smaller leaves and a different flowering and fruiting pattern, is common at higher elevations (1550–1800 m). *Ocotea endresiana*, found above 1550 m, is a very similar species with leaf blades that distinctly curl under at the base.

Comments. This is the most common species of Lauraceae in the upper community and lower Preserve. The anthers of Lauraceae are worth inspecting with a hand lens to observe the odd flaps that cover tiny pockets of pollen. The small, erect fruits held above the leaves are eaten by more birds (18 species) than any other species of Lauraceae and they are important in the diet of the quetzal during the breeding season. The light, cream wood is commonly used for general construction and interior paneling, but it is considered inferior to many other species of ira.

135

Panopsis suaveolens   *Papa*
Proteaceae – Protea and Macadamia family   "Potato"

Description. A large canopy tree (15–40 m); LEAVES to 4 x 12 cm, spiraled and bunched at the twig tips, oblong and widest at or beyond the middle with a blunt tip, glabrous; FLOWERS white with 4 narrow curled petals with the stamens attached near the tips, set in pairs along a long, unbranched spike; FRUIT a green to brown, lemon-shaped woody ball with a nipple at the tip, up to 5 cm, does not open, 1 seed.

Habitat and Phenology. Occasional to common in mature forest at 1300–1700 m. FL: JUN–AUG; FR: FEB, APR–JUL, SEP.

Similar species. *Roupala glaberrima* (danto), another Proteaceae at Monteverde, has flowers like those of *Panopsis*, but the fruits are 3 cm flat pods that open to release two winged seeds. Although used for construction, many people develop a rash from contact with the sap and sawdust of *Roupala*.

Comments. The flowers are fragrant at night and attract moths. Old fruits under the trees are often chewed open by agoutis— their tooth marks clearly engraved on the woody surface. The Spanish name originates from the potato-like taste of the seed that is eaten either raw or fried. The hard wood is used for construction and furniture.

Persea americana   *Aguacate*
Lauraceae – Laurel and Avocado family   Wild avocado

Description. A medium to large tree (10–30 m); LEAVES to 9 x 15 cm, broadly elliptic to obovate with long petioles, a gray-green color on the leaf underside; small yellow-green FLOWERS in long inflorescences that stand out beyond the leaves; FRUIT a large green to brown ball (3–5 cm), with a thick leathery rind enclosing a single large round seed (avocado pit).

Habitat and Phenology. Common to occasional in forest edge and pasture areas and occasionally growing as a canopy tree in mature forest at 1200–1500 m; down to 1000 m in the San Luis Valley. FL: FEB–MAY; FR: OCT–JAN.

Similar species. Another questionably distinct species (referable to *P. nubigena*) with larger leaves (to 14 x 25 cm) and fruit (5–8 cm) occurs from 1450–1600 m. *P. schiedeana*, with round, pubescent leaves and large round fruit, is a common canopy tree in the high cloud forest.

Comments. This tree is the progenitor of our commercial avocado, which was brought into cultivation by the pre-Colombian inhabitants of Central America. Most individuals are leafless for a short time during the dry season. Flowering occurs just as the trees flush a new set of leaves. As in other Lauraceae, the flowers attract a variety of small diurnal insects such as flies, bees, beetles, wasps, and butterflies. The fruits are apparently adapted for dispersal by arboreal mammals, and Allen (1956) noted that spider monkeys are fond of them. The high tensile strength of the wood makes it valuable for the construction of oxen yokes. It is also excellent for furniture and paneling.

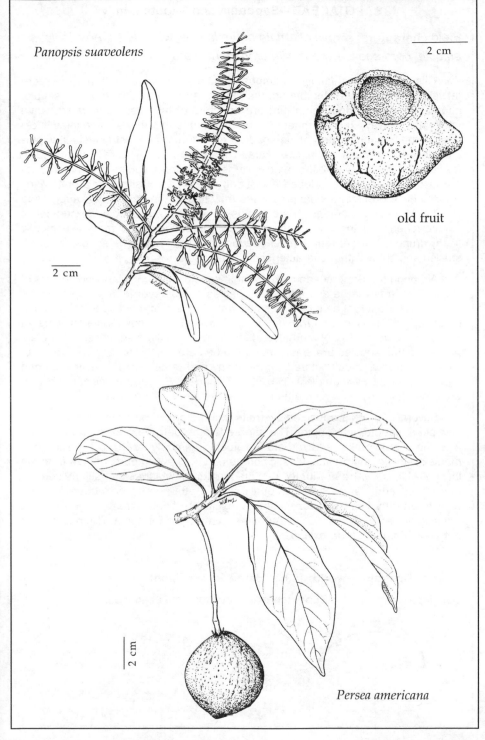

Panopsis suaveolens

2 cm

old fruit

2 cm

Persea americana

2 cm

SAPOTACEAE—Sapodilla and Sapote family

Field characters: *simple alternate entire leaves, white latex, no stipules, smooth, hard-shelled seeds with prominent scars.*

This small tropical family is composed mainly of tree species that are vegetatively inconspicuous. Members of the family can be recognized by the simple, alternate leaves without teeth that are bunched at twig tips or spiraled, white latex (often slowly exuded), inner bark mottled red, and either with petioles thickened in the basal half (pop-bottle-shaped) as in *Pouteria* or with clusia-like, parallel secondary veins as in *Manilkara*. The flowers are generally arranged in fascicles along the twigs either among or below the leafy segments. The corollas are mostly small, white, 5-lobed and fused at the base, falling as a unit. Many species have odd staminodal processes attached to the corolla and alternating with the functional stamens. The stamens are equal to or double the number of corolla lobes and the style is simple and unbranched. The fruits are mostly fleshy drupes or large, round, multi-seeded fleshy "berries." The seeds are hard-shelled and shiny with a characteristic hilum or scar.

Although the Sapotaceae are richest in species in the lowland wet forests of Costa Rica, a few large and abundant species at Monteverde make up a significant part of the forest canopy. The small white flowers of most species are pollinated by stingless bees (*Trigona*) in our area. The 1 cm tubular flowers of *Pouteria fossicola* are nocturnal and presumably pollinated by small moths. Fruits of some species are small enough to be eaten by birds (*Sideroxylon*), but most are large and dull-colored with a fleshy rind reminiscent of avocados and these are eaten by mammals. Two of our species, *Pouteria fossicola* and *Sideroxylon stenospermum,* are among the largest trees of the area.

Several species produce edible fruits that are grown on a small scale (sapodilla plum, sapote, star apple). The sapote is a grapefruit-sized, round fruit with a leathery brown skin and red-orange flesh commonly seen in the San José markets. Chicle, the original elastic component of chewing gum, comes from the latex of *Manilkara*. Trees with tell-tale diagonal trunk slashes can still be seen at Palo Verde and Santa Rosa National Parks. Gutta-percha, a rubber-like substance formerly important for electrical insulation, comes from the latex of an Asian species (*Palaquium*). Several species are used for construction lumber in our area (*Pouteria*, *Sideroxylon*).

Species Diversity—World: 1000; **Costa Rica:** 56; **Monteverde:** 13

See page listings under **Sapotaceae** in index for local examples.

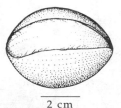

Sapote seed

2 cm

138

Pouteria fossicola
Sapotaceae – Sapodilla and Sapote family

Zapote
Sapote

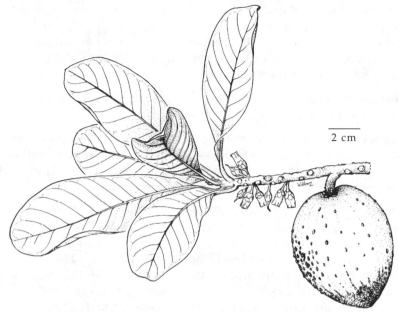

2 cm

Description. A large canopy tree (20–40 m); inner bark pink, exuding white latex; large LEAVES to 5 x 14 cm, spiraled and bunched at the twig tips, widest beyond the middle with rounded tip and gradually narrowing base, no marginal teeth, stiff and glabrous; 1 cm tubular cream-white FLOWERS clustered along the twigs, fragrant at night; FRUIT a spherical to elliptic hard ball, 7–12 cm long, green or brown with warty lenticels, containing 1–2 large shiny brown seeds each with a large elliptic tan scar.

Habitat and Phenology. Common in mature forest at 1400–1600 m; also on Atlantic slope. FL: APR–MAY, JUL, SEP–OCT; FR: MAY–FEB (most of year).

Similar species. Even with its large fruits, obovate leaves, and white latex, the sapote can easily be confused with *Persea americana* (generally with more oval leaves and globose fruit). *Meliosma vernicosa*, with similarly shaped leaves, but lacking white latex, produces 3 cm round fruit on terminal infructescences. Other species of Sapotaceae in the area have smaller leaves and fruits. The smooth-shelled seed with an oval scar identifies this species.

Comments. The fragrant flowers are nocturnal and apparently pollinated by moths. Arboreal mammals and agoutis eat the fruits. The edible flesh of the fruit, which turns orange-yellow at maturity, is hard to find in ripe condition. A related species, *Pouteria sapota*, is grown commercially for its edible fruit, which is sold at fruit stands around San José. Both immature and mature seeds release the bitter almond odor of cyanide when cut open.

139

Quararibea costaricensis *Molenillo*
Bombacaceae – Kapok-tree family "Mixer"

Description. A subcanopy tree (15–25 m); TRUNK shallowly fluted with smooth cinnamon and gray flaking bark; BRANCHES horizontal and well spaced; LEAVES to 10 x 20 cm, often drooping, oblong with short petioles arising in a plane; 3 cm white FLOWERS with curled petals and an exserted style and staminal tube with many small anthers at its tip, a sweet fragrance; FRUIT a 3 cm elliptical yellow drupe.

Habitat and Phenology. Common in mature forest at 1500–1550 m, also on the Atlantic slope. FL: FEB–JUL; FR: SEP–NOV.

Similar species. The smooth, fluted trunk, showing a calico pattern of red-brown and gray where the thin bark has flaked off, is similar to several species of Myrtaceae. The pagoda-like branching pattern is a good field identification character. *Q. funebris* occurs at 900 m in the San Luis Valley.

Comments. The peeling bark sheds epiphytes, making the bare trunk conspicuous among the moss-covered trees in this habitat. The pleasantly fragrant flowers, which open in the evening, attract hawk moths during the night and hummingbirds and butterflies in the morning. The soft, cream wood has a fine, straight grain. The wood is not used for fires because the smoke is irritating to the eyes. The local name refers to use of small branches (with perpendicular twigs) for mixing chocolate and fruit shakes.

Quercus corrugata *Roble*
Fagaceae – Beech and Oak family Ridge oak

Description. A large canopy tree (20–35 m); LEAVES to 6 x 19 cm, spiraled and bunched at the twig tips, widest near the middle, teeth usually evident only on saplings and suckers, nearly glabrous, stipules; small yellow-green FLOWERS, the males on dangling 6 cm catkins, the females in leaf axils near the twig tips; FRUITS are typical acorns, 3 cm long.

Habitat and Phenology. Common on ridges and peaks in the cloud forest, especially those exposed to the mists carried by the trade winds (1550–1800 m). FL: MAR–MAY; FR: SEP–NOV.

Similar species. Three other species of oaks occur at Monteverde, but the only similar one is *Q. insignis*, which grows at lower elevations, has pubescent leaves with dull teeth, and very large (3–4 cm) acorns. The other two species are black oaks with narrow, glabrous leaves with pointed teeth and small (2 cm) acorns.

Comments. This is the large, gnarly trunked oak seen in the Preserve. The trunk is usually buttressed and the branches twisted and covered with epiphytes. Oaks are wind-pollinated. The acorns accumulate under the trees where at least remnant fruit cupules can usually be found. Like temperate oaks, the wood is hard and very durable, but it tends to twist badly on drying. It is used for jobs like cross beams in bridges where resistance to rotting is especially important.

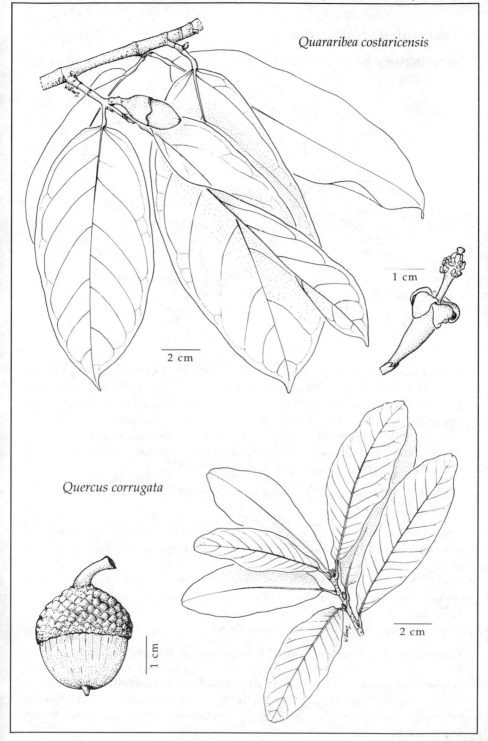

Quararibea costaricensis

2 cm

1 cm

Quercus corrugata

1 cm

2 cm

Sideroxylon stenospermum
Sapotaceae – Sapodilla and Sapote family

Tempisque
Tempisque

fruit with calyx

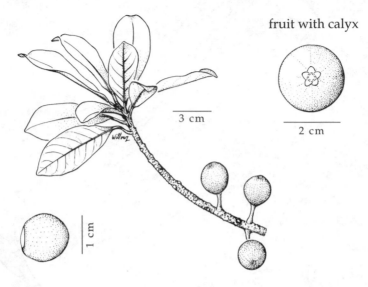

3 cm

2 cm

1 cm

Description. A very large canopy tree (20–40 m); TRUNK straight, without buttresses, with rough or checked black bark, exuding white latex when cut; LEAVES bunched at the twig tips, to 3 x 8 cm, widest beyond the middle, without teeth, the underside of young leaves with a carpet of white and rust hairs (lost in old leaves); small white FLOWERS in dense clusters along the twigs often below the leafy nodes, fragrant; FRUIT a 2 cm round black drupe, the shiny brown-black seed with a small oval scar.

Habitat and Phenology. Occasional in mature wet forest at 1300–1500 m. FL: JUL–SEP; FR: MAR–MAY.

Similar species. Reaching more than a meter in diameter, this is an impressive tree distinct from most other species. The shaggy or checked, black bark is characteristic in large individuals. Seeds can often be found scattered under the tree, helping with identification. Some sympatric Sapotaceae include *Pouteria reticulata* with reddish bark, elliptic leaves and more elongate fruits and seeds than the tempisque and *P. exfoliata* with scalloped bark, small elliptic leaves, and 3 cm round yellow fruits.

Comments. The fragrant, diurnal flowers attract stingless bees in large numbers. The hard, cream-colored wood, used locally for general construction, is said to rot quickly unless it is kept dry. The wood is used green because after drying it is too hard to nail. Newly cut logs are very attractive to two species of metallic purple long-horned beetles (Cerambycidae), locally called "tempisque beetles."

142

Sloanea ampla *Peine de mico*

Elaeocarpaceae – Elaeocarpus family "Monkey comb"

Description. A medium to large canopy tree (20–30 m); large, oblong LEAVES to 25 x 40 cm, without teeth, the long petioles thickened at the base and apex and the blade angled upward from the petiole tip; small cream FLOWERS with many anthers and lacking petals, fragrant; FRUIT a large, 6–8 cm red capsule covered with long spines, opening into 4 valves, the valves red inside, the seed white with an orange aril.

Habitat and Phenology. Occasional at 1400–1550 m; more common on the Atlantic slope. FL: FEB–MAY; FR: NOV–JAN.

Similar species. Two other species occur in the area. *Sloanea faginea* has 4 cm fruits and smaller leaves than *S. ampla*; *S. brenesii* has small, pubescent opposite leaves and spiny, 2 cm fruit.

Comments. The large leaf with uptilted blade stands out, but the spiny, red fruits are more conspicuous. In the past, the annual crop of *S. ampla* fruits attracted flocks of great green macaws (Wolf Guindon and Eladio Cruz, pers. comm.). Now they are eaten by black guans and parrots. Although these trees reach a great size, the wood is low in quality and lacks durability.

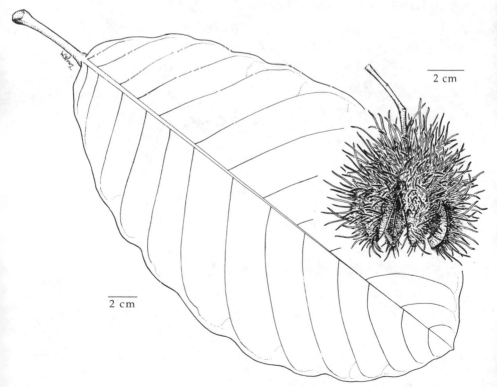

2 cm

2 cm

143

GROUP 10.
LEAVES ALTERNATE WITHOUT TEETH, VENATION PINNATE, LEAF BLADES WIDEST AT OR BELOW THE MIDDLE

typical *Acnistus* leaf with galls

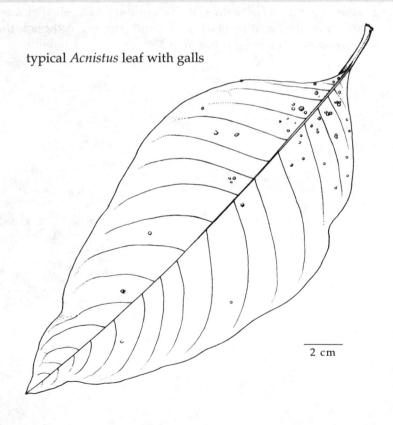

2 cm

Acnistus arborescens
Solanaceae – Nightshade and Tomato family

Güitite

Guitite

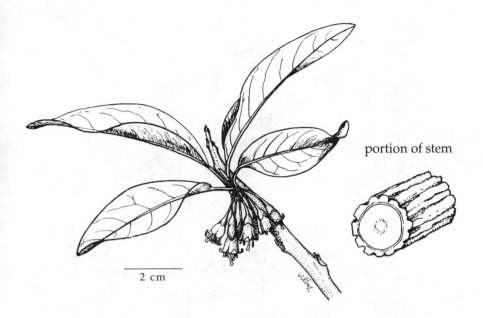

portion of stem

2 cm

Description. A small pasture tree (2–10 m); TRUNK with corky, deeply fissured beige bark; LEAVES variable in size, but mostly large (to 25 cm), soft, glabrous; dense clusters of 1 cm bell-shaped white FLOWERS along the twigs among or below the leaves; FRUIT a 7 mm orange berry with many small flat seeds.

Habitat and Phenology. Common in pastures and overgrown roadsides from 800–1500 m. FL: MAY–JUN; FR: JUL–SEP; often with sporadic individuals flowering out of synchrony with the main population.

Similar species. Because of its habitat and distinctive features this species is hard to confuse with any other tree. Most individuals have at least some leaves with small, wart-like galls.

Comments. The flowers are diurnal and attract a wide variety of insects, including bees, butterflies, wasps, beetles, and flies as well as occasional hummingbirds. Over 40 species of birds have been recorded eating the fruits. Thus, the species provides resources for a wide variety of wildlife. Güitite cuttings can be planted as a living fence post and the corky bark serves as an ideal substrate for growing epiphytic orchids. Children commonly eat the fruits.

145

Ardisia compressa *Tucuico*

Myrsinaceae – Myrsine family

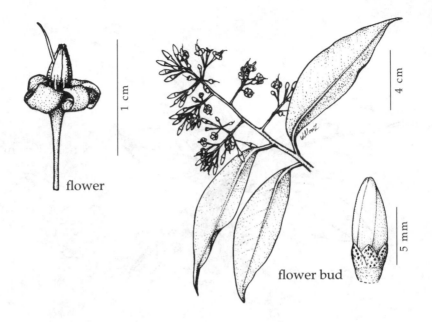

flower

flower bud

Description. An understory treelet (3–8 m); LEAVES to 6 x 14 cm, widest at the middle, margin entire or with obscure rounded teeth, often leathery, lateral veins obscure, glabrous, yellow translucent dots or steaks; FLOWERS 8 mm long with 5 white recurved petals and yellow anthers; FRUIT a purple-black berry, 6–8 mm with 1 seed.

Habitat and Phenology. Common in primary forest and old secondary forest at 1200–1600 m. FL: sporadic, MAY, OCT–NOV; FR: MAR–JUN, JUL–SEP.

Similar species. Several other species of *Ardisia* occur here, all with similar flowers and fruits, but differing in leaf shape. *A. palmana*, a subcanopy tree of the cloud forest, has large oblong leaves held in a plane. *A. solomonii*, a common understory tree along the Continental Divide, has 20 cm leaves bunched at the twig tips.

Comments. Conspicuous in flower or fruit, this is otherwise a rather drab treelet. The "buzz" flowers produce only pollen (no nectar), which issues in a cloud from tiny terminal pores in the anthers when the flower is vibrated by a perching bee. Some of the pollen collects on the hairy body of the bee, which it later combs off and stores in its pollen baskets. The seeds are dispersed by birds, such as the long-tailed manakin.

146

Ardisia palmana *Tucuico*

Myrsinaceae – Myrsine family

Description. A subcanopy tree, 8–20 m; large smooth narrowly elliptic LEAVES with inconspicuous secondary veins, to 9 x 30 cm, held in a plane, minute brown spots on lower surface; many small FLOWERS with 5 white petals and yellow anthers in large much-branched inflorescences at twig tips; FRUIT a small round black berry with 1 seed.

Habitat and Phenology. Common in the cloud forest above 1500 m, especially in older light gaps. FL: OCT–NOV, but sporadic in other months; FR: JAN–MAY.

Similar species. It would be hard to confuse this tree with any others in the area. The Christmas tree-like branching pattern is distinctive with the more or less horizontal branches longer at the bottom and shorter toward the top. With a sample in hand, note the smooth, fleshy leaves with scimitar-shaped leaf buds. The transparent dots and streaks, characteristic of Myrsinaceae, are difficult to see through the thick leaves.

Comments. The flowers are pollinated by bees that buzz them to collect the pollen (see *Ardisia compressa*). The edible fruits attract many species of birds including the occasional black guan and resplendent quetzal.

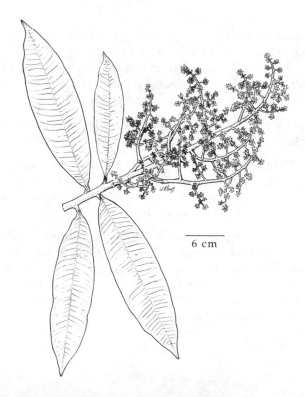

6 cm

147

Bourreria costaricensis
Boraginaceae – Borage family

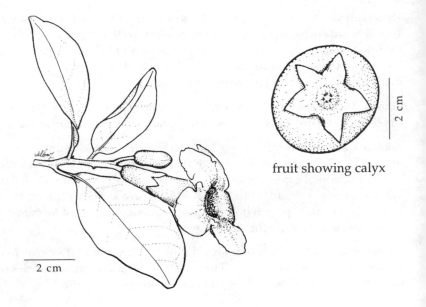

fruit showing calyx

2 cm

Description. A medium to large tree (15–40 m); TRUNK deeply channeled with finely flaking beige bark; LEAVES to 7 x 10 cm, broadly elliptic, glabrous with poorly defined secondary veins, somewhat fleshy; large white FLOWERS to 4 cm long with 5 lobes, forked style, large calyx split into irregular lobes; FRUIT a fleshy berry to 4 cm diameter, purple-green with 4 seeds.

Habitat and Phenology. Occasional in mature forest, edges and pastures at 1300–1500 m. FL and FR: most of year, but especially in wet season.

Similar species. The rather nondescript leaves could be confused with some figs (white latex), *Ardisia* (translucent dots), *Prunus* (bitter almond odor and nectar glands) or Lauraceae (avocado odor). The fluted trunk and beige bark are good field marks for large individuals.

Comments. The flowers are pollinated at night by hawk moths (Sphingidae). While the broad corolla tube suggests a bat flower, we have not observed bats visiting at this tree. Because the fruits are too large for birds to swallow, we suspect they may be eaten by mammals; however, we know of no observations to support this idea. Because the fruits require many months to mature, most trees have fruits in some stage of development.

Cestrum sp. *Zorrillo*
Solanaceae – Nightshade and Tomato family

Description. A treelet or small tree (3–8 m); leathery lance-shaped LEAVES to 4 x 16 cm with an acute to rounded base; pale green, cream or maroon FLOWERS with narrow 2 cm long tubes and 5 short lobes, strongly scented at night; FRUIT a small black berry with 1–12 angular seeds shaped like pieces of broken pottery.

Habitat and Phenology. Common in open understory of mature forest, secondary forest and edge at 1300–1500 m. FL: sporadic, DEC–JAN; FR: MAR–MAY.

Similar species. Nine species of *Cestrum* occur in our area. All are shrubs or small trees with fragrant, tubular flowers adapted for pollination by nocturnal moths. Some have purple-black fruits, while others produce spongy, white fruits.

Comments. This species can be conspicuous either when flowering or fruiting. A flowering episode may last less than a week. The flowers are clustered all along the twigs and branches in dense, short inflorescences. The flowers last for several days, opening at night and closing again during the day. The fruits are eaten by birds.

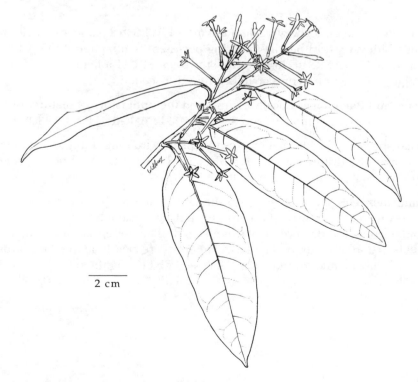

2 cm

149

Erythroxylum macrophyllum
Erythroxylaceae – Coca family

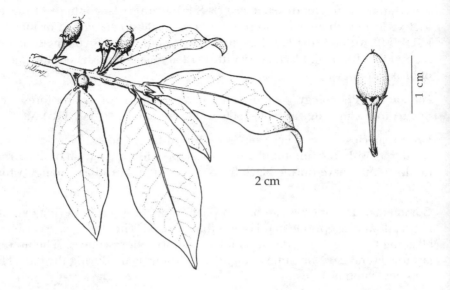

2 cm

1 cm

Description. An understory treelet (2–6 m); LEAVES in a plane, to 4 x 10 cm, elliptic with very short petioles, bearing persistent 6 mm papery STIPULES; small white FLOWERS in clusters along the twigs; FRUIT a 1 cm elliptic drupe changing from green to orange to bright red, 1-seeded.

Habitat and Phenology. Locally common in the understory of mature forest at 1200–1400 m (common at Bajo del Tigre). FL: MAR–JUN; FR: JUL–SEP.

Similar species. The alternate leaves in a plane with long triangular stipules in the axils are distinctive. From a distance this species could be confused with *Psychotria*, which has opposite leaves.

Comments. This species belongs to the same genus as the South American *E. coca*, which is the source of the notorious drug, cocaine. Our local species is said to contain little or none of this alkaloid. The flowers are pollinated by small bees and other diurnal insects. The fruits are clearly adapted for birds, but only the emerald toucanet has been recorded eating them.

150

Ficus crassiuscula *Chilamate*
Moraceae – Fig and Mulberry family

Description. A large, free-standing canopy tree (20–35 m); copious cream-white latex; narrow STIPULES to 7 cm; LEAVES to 7 x 16 cm, shiny and fleshy; tiny FLOWERS lining the inside of the globose, fruit-like inflorescence (syconium); FRUIT 4–6 cm, globose, yellow-green and warty.

Habitat and Phenology. Common in the higher cloud forest above 1550 m, especially in sites exposed to the trade winds. FL: FEB–APR; FR: MAY–JUL, OCT–JAN.

Similar species. While *F. crassiuscula* is a free-standing tree, the base of the trunk is often channeled and irregular, indicating its beginnings as a strangling vine growing on a fallen log or live tree trunk. The smooth, gray bole contrasts with *F. tuerckheimii* and *F. hartwegii*, which are hemi-epiphyte stranglers with small fruits, oval leaves and ropy, fluted trunks formed from coalesced aerial roots. *Ficus macbridei*, with smaller fruit and large oval leaves, is a small, free-standing tree that grows in light gaps of the high cloud forest. *Sapium* spp. also have white latex, smooth, elliptic leaves, and gray bark; but the petiole has a pair of nectar glands and the large stipules are lacking.

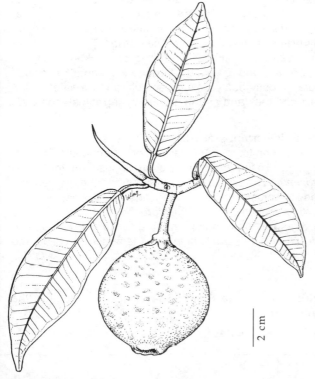

Comments. This is one of the most prominent, large trees of the high cloud forest, although one often spots the rotting fruits on the ground first. Monkeys and other arboreal mammals eat the figs in the tree, while peccaries forage on the fallen fruits. The soft, white wood is used for low level construction jobs such as concrete forms.

2 cm

151

MORACEAE—Fig and Mulberry family

Field characters: *simple, alternate leaves with a marginal vein, white or cream latex, conical stipules at twig tips, unisexual flowers lacking showy corollas, 1-seeded fleshy fruits, or figs.*

The Moraceae are mostly trees and shrubs. One genus found in our area (*Dorstenia*) is an understory herb. *Cecropia*, a genus formerly included in the Moraceae, was moved to its own small segregate family, Cecropiaceae. The Moraceae are fairly uniform vegetatively in having simple alternate leaves with pinnate venation (often with a prominent collecting vein), deciduous conical stipules, and white or cream-colored latex. The leaves may be toothed or entire, and either pubescent or glabrous. The flowers are unisexual and lack showy corollas. They are usually in groups of dense, head-like or catkin-like inflorescences and these often have overlapping bracts at the base.

The majority of Moraceae are wind-pollinated and many are dioecious (*Pseudolmedia*, *Sorocea* and *Trophis* in our area) or monoecious (*Brosimum*). In contrast, all figs have tiny wasp pollinators (family Agaonidae). If you cut open a mature fig, you will see a mixture of spent flowers and seeds covering the inside of the fruit rind and possibly some tiny, black wasps with slender ovipositors. These are the specialized fig pollinators, and possibly some of their wasp parasites (with much longer ovipositors). The female wasps must leave the fig fruits just before they mature or they will be eaten by seed dispersers. At this time, the male flowers mature and shed pollen, which the female wasps collect in tiny pockets on their bodies. Then the little wasps fly to another fig tree in a stage with female flowers where they pollinate the flowers and oviposit. Fruits of Moraceae are typically fleshy and one-seeded except for figs, which are aggregates of numerous small fruits each containing one tiny seed and function in seed dispersal like berries. The fruits of our species are all animal-dispersed; the smaller ones, red or black in color, are eaten by birds (*Sorocea*, *Trophis*, some *Ficus*), the larger ones (some *Ficus* spp., *Naucleopsis*, *Pseudolmedia*), mostly dull yellow-green colored, are eaten in the trees by arboreal mammals and bats and on the ground by terrestrial mammals such as peccaries.

This family represents an important proportion of the trees in most tropical forests. Although white latex is often toxic, as in many Apocynaceae and Euphorbiaceae, some Moraceae (e.g., *Brosimum utile*) have innocuous latex that local people drink like milk. *Brosimum* leaves are fed to cattle during the dry season. A few species of *Ficus* produce commercially important figs, and the genus, *Artocarpus,* yields breadfruit. While *Maclura* (formerly *Chlorophora*) is used for wood in Costa Rica, the family does not yield much timber. *Castilla* and *Ficus* have been used as a source of rubber. *Ficus benjamina* is the famous evergreen tree of shopping malls.

Species Diversity—World: 1200; **Costa Rica:** 86 (48 of these belong to the largest genus, *Ficus*); **Monteverde:** 43

See page listings under **Moraceae** in index for local examples.

152

Ficus tuerckheimii

Moraceae – Fig and Mulberry family

Higuerón

Strangler fig

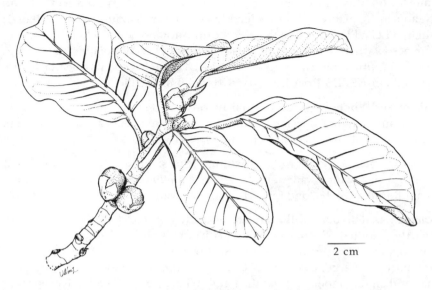

2 cm

Description. A large canopy tree (20–40 m), TRUNK fluted and buttressed, often with a mixture of rope-like, partly fused roots and channeled stems, smooth bark, all parts exuding copious white latex; LEAVES to 8 x 12 cm, oval to round with a rounded to weakly lobed base, thick and rubbery, glabrous; FLOWERS tiny, crowded inside a hollow green 1 cm fruit-like inflorescence; FRUIT an off-round 1.5 cm dark red berry containing many tiny seeds and spent male flowers, the base with large papery bracts that cover half the fruit.

Habitat and Phenology. Common in pastures and forest from 1300–1550 m. FL: AUG–OCT; FR: APR–MAY, SEP–DEC (fruiting is sporadic).

Similar species. Other stranglers here include *F. hartwegii*, a rare species with smaller glabrous leaves, *F. velutina*, with large, densely pubescent leaves and pubescent green fruit with yellow spots, and *F. pertusa*, a smaller species common below 1450 m, with small, elliptic, glabrous leaves and 1–1.5 cm reddish green figs.

Comments. This is one of the largest trees in the area. The ropy, partly coalesced roots and hollow trunk are characteristic of this and other strangler figs. Except for *F. crassiuscula*, the plants begin as epiphytes, growing from seeds defecated by animals that eat the figs. As the plant grows, it drops slender aerial roots to the ground to increase its water and nutrient uptake. The roots gradually fuse together to form a tight wrapping around the trunk of the host tree. This and the shading of its crown will eventually kill the host tree, whose trunk rots away leaving the hollow fig tree.

153

Guatteria verrucosa *Anonillo, Malagueto*
Annonaceae – Custard apple family

Description. A subcanopy tree (8–20 m), LEAVES to 5 x 14 cm held in a plane, with a very short petiole, blade elongate elliptic, without teeth, leathery, appearing glabrous (but underside covered with minute orange hairs); solitary FLOWERS in leaf axils, green and photosynthetic when immature, 3 cm across when mature with 6 fleshy yellow petals (3 opening flat, 3 held erect), emitting a pleasing fruity odor; FRUIT in clusters, purple-black, globose, 1.5 cm; SEEDS 1 per fruit, flat with a pebbly surface.

Habitat and Phenology. Occasional in open forest and edge from 1400–1700 m, and Atlantic slope; most common on exposed peaks and in the swamp. FL: all year, peak from JAN–APR; FR: AUG–SEP, NOV–APR.

Similar species. A species with very similar leaves, but smaller fruits occurs in the Río Peñas Blancas valley at 700–900 m. *Mollinedia pinchotiana* (Monimiaceae) found in high cloud forest has similar fruits.

Comments. The mature flowers are actually "open" when they are closed, while the buds have the petals spread horizontally and look open. We suspect that nocturnal beetles pollinate these flowers as they do other species of Annonaceae. Large, frugivorous birds, e.g., the resplendent quetzal, black guan and emerald toucanet, eat the fruit. What appear to be small clusters of fruit are actually individual, separate maturing ovaries (fruitlets) of a single flower. The Annonaceae is one of several primitive families of angiosperms in which the ovaries are incompletely fused.

Magnolia poasana
Magnoliaceae – Magnolia family Magnolia

Description. A subcanopy tree of 10–20 m; LEAVES to 5 x 12 cm, elliptic, a prominent stipule scar circling the twig below each petiole; large white FLOWERS 10 cm in diameter with 6 spatulate petals and 3 gray membranous sepals; FRUIT a 4 cm cone-like aggregate of dehiscing capsules, with the exserted seeds covered with bright red arils and dangling from threads.

Habitat and Phenology. Rarely seen except along Sendero Pantanoso and on Cerro Amigos at 1600–1800 m. FL: NOV–JUL, peak FEB–APR; FR: JUL–AUG.

Similar species. *Talauma gloriensis*, with white flowers and similar fruits, has larger, dark green leaves and the petiole has an elongate stipule scar on the dorsal side.

Comments. The flowers are presumed to attract beetles at night, as is the case with other species in this genus. One often notices the fallen petals before finding the tree itself. The dehisced fruits are rather bizarre.

154

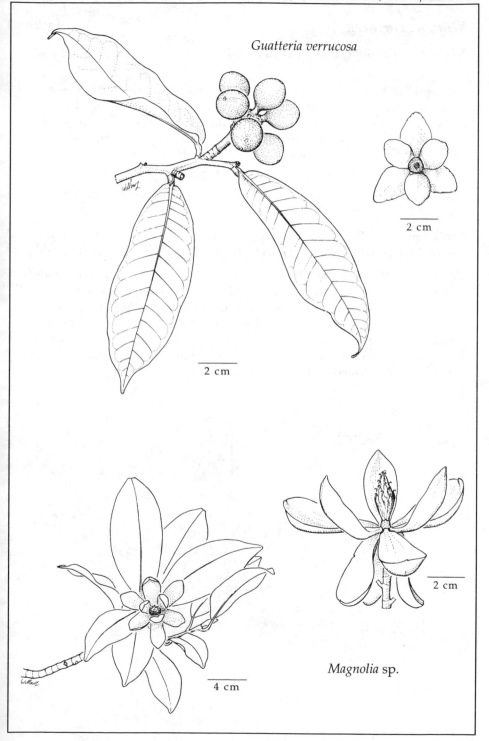

Guatteria verrucosa

2 cm

2 cm

Magnolia sp.

4 cm

2 cm

Myrsine coriacea
Myrsinaceae – Myrsine family

Ratoncillo
"Little mouse"

Description. A small to medium tree (5–25 m); LEAVES to 2 x 8 cm, spiraled in dense clusters at twig tips, underside much paler, without teeth, lateral veins obscure, pubescent mainly on the petiole, translucent red or yellow dots and streaks; dioecious; tiny 3 mm FLOWERS, with 4–5 green petals, clustered along twigs often below the leafy segments; FRUIT a 3–4 mm black 1-seeded berry in dense clusters along leafless sections of twigs.

Habitat and Phenology. Common in pastures, secondary forest, and along the road in the Preserve, from 1200–1600 m. FL: MAR–JUL; FR: SEP–DEC.

Similar species. *Drymis granadensis* (Winteraceae) found in the elfin forest and on high peaks has larger leaves with a similar shape and pale underside.

Comments. *Myrsine* is one of the most abundant pasture/edge trees around Monteverde. The dense fruit clusters along the twigs and small, bunched, elliptic leaves with pale undersides are distinctive. Being dioecious, only about half the individuals produce fruit. The fruit are eaten by at least ten species of birds and are especially favored by clay-colored robins. Brown jays sometimes break off fruiting twigs and carry them to sturdier perches where they pick off the fruits at a leisurely pace.

2 cm

156

Ocotea whitei

Ira rosa, Ira rosada

Lauraceae – Laurel and Avocado family

Ira rosa

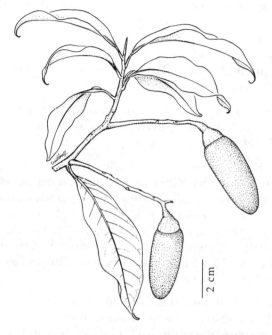

Description. A large canopy tree with light brown, finely flaking bark; LEAVES to 2.5 x 9 cm with a twisted drip tip; tiny yellow-orange FLOWERS in large inflorescences; pendant, elliptical black FRUIT 3–4 cm long, with a red cupule.

Habitat and Phenology. Formerly common around the Monteverde community at 1300–1500 m. FL: MAR–AUG; FR: APR–AUG.

Similar species. Several sympatric species of Lauraceae have generally similar leaves and fruits, including *Nectandra salicina, N. smithii, Ocotea meziana,* and *O. monteverdensis.* The Lauraceae are notoriously difficult to identify. Even identification to genus is certain only with flowering material. However, one can learn to identify sterile and fruiting specimens at a site by individual species characteristics. Burger and van der Werff (1990) provide technical keys and descriptions for most Costa Rican Lauraceae.

Comments. The yellow crowns are conspicuous during flowering. The fruits are a staple in the diet of the quetzal immediately following the nesting season (July–August). The dark red wood is favored for furniture making and flooring. This species was formerly an abundant canopy tree in this area, but most have been cut for lumber.

157

Prunus annularis   *Duraznillo*

Rosaceae – Rose and Apple family   Wild cherry

Description. A small to medium tree (7–20 m); shredded twigs and leaves with the bitter almond odor of cyanide; LEAVES to 5 x 10 cm, held in a plane, elliptic, widest at or below the middle with a narrow tip, glabrous; small white FLOWERS with 5 petals and about 20 stamens crowded along short erect spikes, very fragrant in daytime; FRUIT a shiny black cherry-sized drupe with one large cream seed with reticulate fibers on surface.

Habitat and Phenology. Common in light gaps and along the forest edge in high cloud forest (1500–1800 m), rarely occurring in ravines down to 1400 m. FL: NOV–FEB; FR: APR–JUN.

Similar species. Several other *Prunus* species occur in the region. All have similar flowers and fruits, but differ in leaf characteristics, seed shape, and especially in the location of small nectar-secreting glands on the underside of the leaf blade. *Prunus annularis* has 1–3 pairs of glands spaced across the basal quarter of the blade; *P. cornifolia* has a pair of glands on the blade margin just above the petiole connection, and the vein axils have tufts of rust-colored hairs; *Prunus* sp. ("big leaf") has a single pair of nectaries in the angle formed by the leaf base and midvein.

Comments. The fragrant diurnal flowers attract small bees, especially *Trigona* spp. Boat-billed flycatchers and toucanets eat the fruits. Despite their close relationship to cherries, the fruits are bitter, tasteless and not sweet, so are considered inedible. The wood, light brown with darker streaks, makes good furniture, but it is somewhat difficult to work.

Prunus sp. seed

5 mm

158

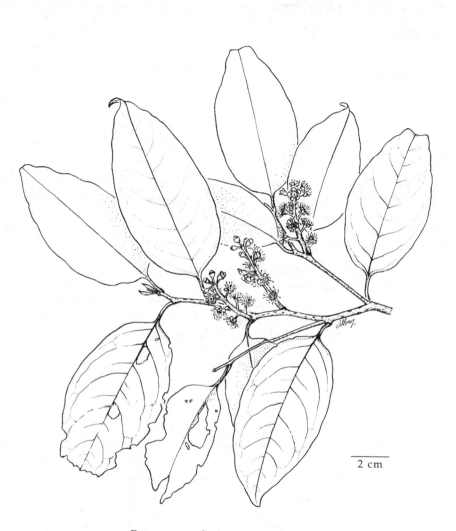

2 cm

Prunus annularis

Solanum aphyodendron
Solanaceae – Nightshade and Tomato family

Description. A treelet (2–5 m); LEAVES to 4 x 12 cm, often paired at a node, lance-shaped, glabrous, with a rank odor when shredded; 1 cm FLOWERS with 5 white corolla lobes, 5 bright yellow anthers; FRUIT a 1.5 cm green to yellow berry with numerous flat seeds.

Habitat and Phenology. Common in old pasture, forest edge and roadside habitat from 1200–1550 m. FL: APR–OCT; FR: AUG–DEC.

Similar species. Several other glabrous and spineless species of *Solanum* treelets occur in the area, including *S. brenesii, pastillum, rovirosanum,* and *tuerckheimii.* Of these, *S. rovirosanum,* with elliptic, 15–30 cm leaves and 2 cm fruit (lower cloud forest) and *S. brenesii* with large, lanceolate leaves (Bajo del Tigre) are the species most likely to be encountered.

Comments. This species was formerly identified as *Solanum nudum,* but that name now applies to a South American plant. This treelet is abundant in areas of early succession. The torn leaves produce a strong, acrid odor. Like other *Solanum* species, the flowers offer pollen as the only reward for pollinators. The pollen issues in a little cloud from apical pores in the anthers when they are vibrated by a bee clinging to the flower. Fruit-eating bats remove the fruits from these plants so consistently that ripe fruits are seldom seen.

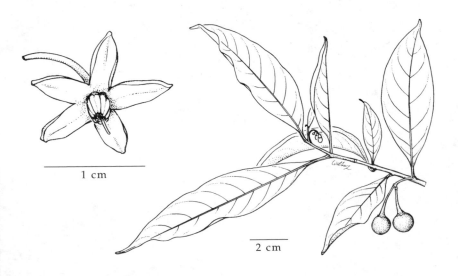

1 cm

2 cm

160

Stauranthus perforatus
Rutaceae – Rue and Citrus family

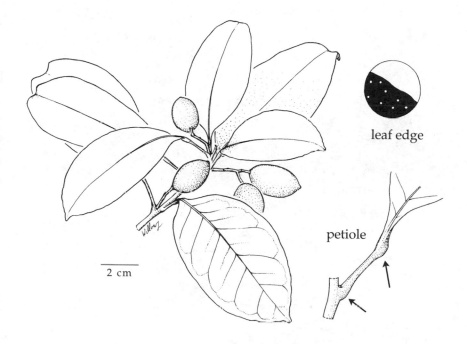

leaf edge

petiole

2 cm

Description. An understory tree (5–15 m); broadly elliptic LEAVES to 7 x 17 cm, entire (or very weakly toothed), the petiole distinctly swollen at each end, the leaves with translucent yellow dots; dioecious; small white FLOWERS in short inflorescences among the leaves; FRUIT a 2 cm purple-black drupe with one seed; seed coat with a reticulate pattern of fibers.

Habitat and Phenology. Common in the understory of mature forest from 1250–1500 m (e.g., Bajo del Tigre). FL: any month, peak DEC–JAN; FR: MAR–JUN.

Similar species. Vegetatively similar to *Hasseltia floribunda*, which has toothed leaves and lacks the yellow oil glands.

Comments. *Stauranthus* tends to branch low on the trunk. The trees are dioecious, producing either male or female flowers. The fruits are eaten by quetzals, toucanets and probably by other large frugivores. The trees are locally abundant in wet forest around the community, but they are inconspicuous until the fruit mature.

161

PART III. Appendices

APPENDIX 1.
TREE SPECIES DESCRIBED IN THIS BOOK
(previously used names appear in parentheses)

Families and Scientific Names	Common Names of Families

ACTINIDIACEAE Actinidia, Kiwi fruit, Saurauia
Saurauia montana Seem., p.124
(*S. pseudoscabrida*, *S. veraguasensis*)

ANACARDIACEAE Cashew, Poison ivy, Mango
Tapirira mexicana Marchand, p.64
(*T. brenesii*)

ANNONACEAE Custard apple, Annona, Pawpaw
Guatteria verrucosa R. E. Fr., p.154
(*G. oliviformis*)

APOCYNACEAE Dogbane, Periwinkle, Oleander
Tabernaemontana longipes Donn. Sm., p.104

ARALIACEAE Ginseng, English ivy, Schefflera
Oreopanax xalapensis (Kunth) Decne. & Planch., p.56

ARECACEAE Palm, Date
Bactris dianeura Burret, p.45
(*B. mexicana*)
Chamaedorea tepejilote Liebm., p.46
Geonoma edulis H. Wendl. ex Spruce, p.46
(*G. seleri*)
Prestoea acuminata (Willd.) H. E. Moore, p.48
(*P. allenii*)

ASTERACEAE Aster, Composite, Daisy
Koanophyllon pittieri (Klatt) R. M. King & H. Rob., p.84
Montanoa guatemalensis B. L. Rob. & Greenm., p.86
Neomirandea angularis (B. L. Rob.) R. M. King & H. Rob., p.87

BIGNONIACEAE Bignonia, Trumpet creeper
Amphitecna haberi A. H. Gentry, sp. nov. ined., p.129
(*Dendrosicus sessilifolius*)

BOMBACACEAE Kapok-tree, Balsa, Bombax
Quararibea costaricensis W. S. Alverson, p.140
(*Q. asterolepis*)

BORAGINACEAE Borage, Heliotrope
Bourreria costaricensis (Standl.) A. H. Gentry, p.148
Cordia cymosa (Donn. Sm.) Standl., p.131

CAPRIFOLIACEAE Honeysuckle, Viburnum
Viburnum costaricanum (Oerst.) Hemsl., p.105

CECROPIACEAE Cecropia
Cecropia obtusifolia Bertol., p.53

163

Families and Scientific Names of the Tree Species Described in this Book	Common Names of Families

CLETHRACEAE — Pepperbush, Clethra
Clethra lanata M. Martens & Galeotti, p.120

CLUSIACEAE — Mangosteen, Garcinia
Clusia stenophylla Standl., p.94
Symphonia globulifera L. f., p.102

CUNONIACEAE — Cunonia
Weinmannia pinnata L., p.68

ELAEOCARPACEAE — Elaeocarpus, Muntingia
Sloanea ampla I. M. Johnst., p.143

ERYTHROXYLACEAE — Coca
Erythroxylum macrophyllum Cav., p.150

EUPHORBIACEAE — Spurge, Poinsettia, Euphorbia
Croton monteverdensis Huft, p.107
Sapium glandulosum (L.) Morong, p.123
   (*S. oligoneurum*)

FABACEAE — Legume
   MIMOSOIDEAE — Acacia, Mimosa
   Inga sierrae Britton & Killip, p.62
      (*I. brenesii*)
   Pithecellobium costaricense (Britton & Rose) Standl.,
   = *Cojoba costaricensis* Britton & Rose, p.62
   PAPILIONOIDEAE — Pea, Bean
   Erythrina lanceolata Standl., p.54
   Styphnolobium monteviridis M. Sousa & Rudd, p.64

FAGACEAE — Beech, Oak
Quercus corrugata Hook., p.140

FLACOURTIACEAE — Flacourtia
Casearia tacanensis Lundell, p.119
Hasseltia floribunda Kunth, p.109

HIPPOCASTANACEAE — Horse-Chestnut, Buckeye
Billia colombiana Planch. & Lindl., p.51

HIPPOCRATEACEAE — Hippocratea
Salacia petenensis Lundell, p.100

LAURACEAE — Laurel, Avocado, Sassafras
Beilschmiedia pendula (Sw.) Hemsl., p.130
   (*B. costaricensis*)
Ocotea tonduzii Standl., p.135
Ocotea whitei Woodson, p.157
Persea americana Mill., p.136

Families and Scientific Names of the Tree Species Described in this Book

Common Names of Families

MAGNOLIACEAE   Magnolia
   Magnolia poasana (Pittier) Dandy, p.154

MALPIGHIACEAE   Barbados cherry, Malpighia
   Bunchosia macrophylla Rose, p.91
      (*B. pilosa*)

MALVACEAE   Mallow, Hibiscus, Cotton
   Hampea appendiculata (Donn. Sm.) Standl., p.108
   Malvaviscus palmanus Pittier & Donn. Sm., p.111

MELASTOMATACEAE   Melastome, Glory bush
   Conostegia oerstediana O. Berg ex Triana, p.81
      (*C. bernoulliana*)
   C. xalapensis (Bonpl.) D. Don, p.83

MELIACEAE   Mahogany, Tropical cedar
   Cedrela tonduzii C. DC., p.59
   Guarea kunthiana A. Juss., p.61
   Trichilia havanensis Jacq., p.66

MONIMIACEAE   Monimia
   Siparuna tonduziana Perkins, p.88

MORACEAE   Fig, Mulberry, Bread fruit
   Ficus crassiuscula Warb. ex Standl., p.151
   F. tuerckheimii Standl., p.153

MYRSINACEAE   Myrsine
   Ardisia compressa Kunth, p.146
   A. palmana Donn. Sm., p.147
   Myrsine coriacea (Sw.) R. Br. ex Roem. & Schult., p.156
      (*Rapanea myricoides*)

MYRTACEAE   Myrtle, Eucalyptus, Guava
   Eugenia guatemalensis Donn. Sm., p.97
   Myrcianthes fragrans (Sw.) McVaugh, p.98

NYCTAGINACEAE   Four-o'clock
   Pisonia sylvatica Standl., p.99

OLEACEAE   Olive
   Chionanthus panamensis (Standl.) Stearn, p.92
      (*C. dominguensis*)

PAPAVERACEAE   Poppy
   Bocconia frutescens L., p.117

PIPERACEAE   Black pepper
   Piper auritum Kunth, p.112

PROTEACEAE   Protea, Macadamia
   Panopsis suaveolens (Klotzsch & H. Karst.) Pittier, p.136

Families and Scientific names of the Tree Species Described in this Book	Common Names of Families

ROSACEAE Rose, Apple, Cherry
  Prunus annularis Koehne, p.158

RUBIACEAE Madder, Coffee, Quinine
  Cosmibuena valerii (Standl.) C. M. Taylor, p.73
    (*Hillia valerii*)
  Elaeagia auriculata Hemsl., p.74
  Gonzalagunia rosea Standl., p.75
  Guettarda poasana Standl., p.76
  Psychotria elata (Sw.) Hammel, p.76
    (*Cephaelis elata*)
  Randia matudae Lorence & Dwyer, p.78
  Rondeletia monteverdensis Lorence, p.79

RUTACEAE Rue, Citrus
  Casimiroa edulis La Llave & Lex., p.52
  Stauranthus perforatus Liebm., p.161
  Zanthoxylum fagara (L.) Sarg., p.68
    (*Z. insulare*)
  Z. juniperinum Poepp., p.70
    (*Z. procerum*)

SABIACEAE Sabia, Snake-seed
  Meliosma idiopoda S. F. Blake, p.120
  M. vernicosa (Liebm.) Griseb., p.133

SAPINDACEAE Soapberry
  Cupania glabra Sw., p.60

SAPOTACEAE Sapodilla, Chicle, Sapote
  Pouteria fossicola Cronquist, p.139
    (*P. viridis*)
  Sideroxylon stenospermum (Standl.) T. D. Penn., p.142
    (*S. portoricense*)

SOLANACEAE Nightshade, Tomato, Tobacco
  Acnistus arborescens (L.) Schltdl., p.145
  Cestrum sp., p.149
    (*C. panamensis, C. racemosum*)
  Solanum aphyodendron S. Knapp, p.160
    (*S. nudum*)

SYMPLOCACEAE Sweetleaf, Symplocos
  Symplocos limoncillo Humb. & Bonpl., p.125

THYMELAEACEAE Mezereum
  Daphnopsis americana (Mill.) J. R. Johnst., p.132
    (*D. seibertii*)

TICODENDRACEAE Ticodendron
  Ticodendron incognitum Gómez-Laur. & L. D. Gómez, p.126

**Families and Scientific names of the
Tree Species Described in this Book**

Common names of Families

TILIACEAE
Heliocarpus americanus L., p.110
(*H. popayanensis*)

Basswood, Linden

ULMACEAE
Trema micrantha (L.) Blume, p.113

Elm

URTICACEAE
Urera elata (Sw.) Griseb., p.114

Nettle

VERBENACEAE
Citharexylum costaricensis Moldenke, p.93
(*C. integerrimum*)

Verbena, Lantana, Teak

APPENDIX 2.

TREES OF THE MONTEVERDE REGION

This list includes trees and treelets reaching 5 meters or more in height that occur on the Pacific slope above 700 m. In some cases, species occur on both slopes, so within the Monteverde region distribution is noted as follows:
P = Pacific slope below 1200 m; **M** = montane area on either slope above 1200 m; **A** = Atlantic slope below 1200 m. **SIZE CLASS: 1**= understory trees and treelets, 3–9 m; **2** = subcanopy trees, 10–20 m; **3** = canopy trees, 20–40 m.

ACANTHACEAE
    Bravaisia integerrima (Spreng.) Standl.   P,2
    Hansteinia sessilifolia Oerst.   P,1
    Spathacanthus hoffmannii Lindau   P,1

ACTINIDIACEAE
    Saurauia montana Seem.   MA,2
        pittieri Donn. Sm.   M,2
        sp. A "Community" (704)   MA,2
        sp. B "Pendant" (9304)   M,1

ANACARDIACEAE
    Anacardium excelsum (Bertero & Balbis ex Kunth) Skeels   P,3
    Astronium graveolens Jacq.   P,3
    Mauria heterophylla Kunth   PM,2
    Tapirira mexicana Marchand   M,3

ANNONACEAE
    Annona pruinosa G. E. Schatz   P,2
    Desmopsis bibracteata (Rob.) Saff.   PM,1
        microcarpa R. E. Fr.   MA,1
    Guatteria verrucosa R. E. Fr.   MA,2

APOCYNACEAE
    Alstonia pittieri (Donn. Sm.) A. H. Gentry   PM,2
    Plumeria rubra L.   P,2
    Rauvolfia aphlebia (Standl.) A. H. Gentry   PA,2
    Stemmadenia donnell-smithii (Rose) Woodson   P,2
        litoralis (Kunth) L. Allorge   PM,2
    Tabernaemontana longipes Donn. Sm.   PM,1

AQUIFOLIACEAE
    Ilex chiriquensis Standl.   M,2
        costaricensis Donn. Sm.   M,3
        haberi (Lundell) W. J. Hahn   PM,3
        hemiepiphytica W. J. Hahn   M,2
        lamprophylla Standl.   M,2
        valerii Standl.   M,2
        vulcanicola Standl.   M,1
        sp. A "No. 6" (10539)   M,3

ARALIACEAE
    Dendropanax arboreus (L.) Decne. & Planch.   MA,3
        gonatopodus (Donn. Sm.) A. C. Sm.   MA,2
        latilobus M. J. Cannon & Cannon   M,2
        querceti Donn. Sm.   MA,1

sp. A (11073)	M,1
Oreopanax capitatus (Jacq.) Decne.	M,2
nubigenus Standl.	M,2
oerstedianus Marchal	M,1
standleyi A. C. Sm.	M,1
vestitus A. C. Sm.	MA,1
xalapensis (Kunth) Decne. & Planch.	PMA,3
Schefflera rodrigueziana Frodin ex M. J. Cannon & Cannon	MA,2

ARECACEAE

Bactris dianeura Burret	M,1
Chamaedorea costaricana Oerst.	PM,1
tepejilote Liebm.	MA,1
Geonoma edulis H. Wendl. ex Spruce	MA,1
Prestoea acuminata (Willd.) H. E. Moore	M,2

ASTERACEAE

Clibadium glomeratum Greenm.	M,1
leiocarpum Steetz	M,1
surinamense L.	M,1
Critonia daleoides DC.	PM,1
hebebotrya DC.	M,2
morifolia (Mill.) R. M. King & H. Rob.	PMA,1
Koanophyllon hylonomum (B. L. Rob.) R. M. King & H. Rob.	M,2
pittieri (Klatt) R. M. King & H. Rob.	M,1
Lasianthaea fruticosa (L.) K. M. Becker	M,1
Montanoa guatemalensis B. L. Rob. & Greenm.	PM,2
tomentosa Cav.	P,1
Neomirandea angularis (B. L. Rob.) R. M. King & H. Rob.	MA,1
Neurolaena lobata (L.) R. Br.	M,1
Podachaenium eminens (Lag.) Sch. Bip.	M,1
Senecio cooperi Greenm.	M,1
copeyensis Greenm.	M,1
sp. A "Ventana" (10853)	M,1
Verbesina oerstediana Benth.	M,1
Vernonia patens Benth.	PM,1

BETULACEAE

Alnus acuminata Kunth	MA,2

BIGNONIACEAE

Amphitecna haberi A. H. Gentry, sp. nov. ined.	MA,2
isthmica (A. H. Gentry) A. H. Gentry, cf.	PM,2
Godmania aesculifolia (Kunth) Standl.	P,2
Tabebuia rosea (Bertol.) DC.	P,2
Tecoma stans (L.) C. Juss. ex Kunth	PM,2

BOMBACACEAE

Bombacopsis quinatum (Jacq.) Dugand	P,3
Ceiba aesculifolia (Kunth) Britt. & Baker	P,2
Ochroma pyramidale (Cav. ex Lam.) Urb.	P,3
Quararibea costaricensis W. S. Alverson	MA,3
funebris (La Llave) Vischer	P,3

BORAGINACEAE
Bourreria costaricensis (Standl.) A. H. Gentry — MA,3
Cordia alliodora (Ruiz & Pav.) Oken — P,2
    croatii James S. Mill. — M,2
    cymosa (Donn. Sm.) Standl. — M,3
    eriostigma Pittier — M,1
    lucidula I. M. Johnst. — P,2
    stellifera I. M. Johnst. — PM,3
Ehretia latifolia DC. — PM,2
Tournefortia glabra L. — PMA,1

BRUNELLIACEAE
Brunellia costaricensis Standl. — M,2

BURSERACEAE
Bursera grandifolia (Schlec.) Engl. — P,2
    simaruba (L.) Sarg. — P,3

CAPPARIDACEAE
Capparis amplissima Lam. — P,1
    cynophallophora L. — P,2
    discolor Donn. Sm. — PMA,2
    frondosa Jacq. — P,1
    mollicella Standl. — P,2
    pringlei Briq. — P,1
Forchhammeria trifoliata Radlk. — PM,2

CAPRIFOLIACEAE
Viburnum costaricanum (Oerst.) Hemsl. — M,2
    stellatotomentosum (Oerst.) Hemsl. — PM,2
    venustum C. V. Morton — M,3

CARICACEAE
Carica cauliflora Jacq. — P,1

CECROPIACEAE
Cecropia obtusifolia Bertol. — PMA,3
    peltata L. — P,3
    polyphlebia Donn. Sm. — M,3

CELASTRACEAE
Crossopetalum tonduzii (Loes.) Lundell — M,2
Euonymus costaricensis Standl. — PM,1
Gymnosporia haberiana Hammel, ined. — M,3
Maytenus reconditus Hammel, ined. — MA,3
    segoviarum Standl. & Steyerm. — P,2
Perrottetia longistylis Rose — PMA,2
Quetzalia occidentalis (Loes.) Lundell — M,2
Zinowiewia costaricensis Lundell — M,1

CHLORANTHACEAE
Hedyosmum costaricense C. E. Wood — MA,2
    goudotianum Solms — M,2

CHRYSOBALANACEAE
Hirtella racemosa Lam. — P,1

170

CLETHRACEAE
   Clethra lanata M. Martens & Galeotti   PM,2
      mexicana A. DC.   M,2

CLUSIACEAE
   Clusia rotundata Standl.   M,1
      stenophylla Standl.   MA,1
      sp. A "near *stenophylla*" (11409)   M,2
      sp. B "Santa Elena" (11552)   PM,2
   Garcinia intermedia (Pittier) Hammel   PMA,2
   Symphonia globulifera L. f.   PMA,2
   Tovomitopsis allenii Maguire   M,3
      glauca Oerst., Planch. & Triana   MA,1
      psychotriifolia Oerst., Planch. & Triana   MA,2
   Vismia ferruginea Kunth   PA,1
      sp. A "Swamp" (9828)   M,2

COCHLOSPERMACEAE
   Cochlospermum vitifolium (Willd.) Spreng.   P,2

COMBRETACEAE
   Terminalia oblonga (Ruiz & Pav.) Steud.   P,3

CORNACEAE
   Cornus disciflora DC.   M,3

CUNONIACEAE
   Weinmannia pinnata L.   MA,3
      wercklei Standl.   M,2

DICHAPETALACEAE
   Dichapetalum axillare Woodson   MA,1

EBENACEAE
   Diospyros nicaraguensis Standl.   P,2
      sp. A "MV" (9895)   M,2
      sp. B "Pointed calyx" (2906)   P,3
      sp. C "Rounded calyx" (1613)   P,3

ELAEOCARPACEAE
   Sloanea ampla I. M. Johnst.   M,2
      brenesii Standl.   M,2
      faginea Standl.   M,3

ERYTHROXYLACEAE
   Erythroxylum macrophyllum Cav.   M,1

EUPHORBIACEAE
   Acalypha leptopoda Müll. Arg.   P,1
      macrostachya Jacq.   PMA,1
      schiedeana Schltdl.   P,1
   Alchornea guatemalensis Lundell   M,1
      latifolia Sw.   MA,3
   Croton draco Cham. & Schltdl.   PM,2
      monteverdensis Huft   M,3
      *niveus Jacq.   M,2
      watsonii Standl.   P,2
      xalapensis Kunth   P,2

Drypetes lateriflora (Sw.) Krug & Urb.	PM,2
sp. A "San Luis" (Bello 35)	P,2
Euphorbia elata Brandegee	M,1
hoffmanniana (Klotzsch & Garcke) Boiss.	PM,1
schlechtendalii Boiss.	P,2
Hyeronima oblonga (Tul.) Müll. Arg.	MA,3
Margaritaria nobilis L. f.	M,2
Ricinus communis L.	M,1
Sapium glandulosum (L.) Morong	M,3
laurifolium (Rich.) Griseb.	MA,3
rigidifolium K. Schum. & Pittier	MA,3
macrocarpum Müll. Arg.	PM,3
Tetrorchidium costaricense Huft	M,2

FABACEAE
  CAESALPINOIDEAE

Senna nicaraguensis (Benth.) Irwin & Barneby	P,2
pallida (Vahl) Irwin & Barneby	P,1
papillosa (Britton & Rose) Irwin & Barneby	P,1

  MIMOSOIDEAE

Acacia angustissima (Mill.) Kuntze	P,2
centralis (Britton & Rose) Lundell	P,2
Albizia adinocephala (Donn. Sm.) Britton & Rose	P,3
Calliandra bijuga Rose	P,2
Cojoba catenata (Donn. Sm.) Britton & Rose	MA,1
costaricensis Britton & Rose	MA,2
Enterolobium cyclocarpum (Jacq.) Griseb.	P,3
Inga longispica Standl.	M,3
marginata Willd.	P,2
micheliana Harms	M,2
mortoniana Jorge León	MA,3
nobilis Willd.	M,2
oerstediana Benth. ex Seem.	PMA,3
punctata Willd.	PM,2
sierrae Britton & Killip	M,2
tonduzii Donn. Sm.	MA,2
Lysiloma divaricatum (Jacq.) J. F. Macbr.	P,3
Samanea saman (Jacq.) Merrill	P,3
Zapoteca formosa (Kunth) H. M. Hern.	P,1
Zygia palmana (Standl.) L. Rico	MA,2

  PAPILIONOIDEAE

Diphysa americana (Mill.) M. Sousa	P,2
humilis Oerst.	P,1
Dussia sp. A (7122)	M,3
Erythrina lanceolata Standl.	PMA,2
Lonchocarpus acuminatus (Schltdl.) M. Sousa	P,2
haberi M. Sousa, ined. (9581)	M,2
oliganthus F. J. Herm.	MA,2
sp. A "MV" (320)	M,3
sp. B "San Luis" (Bello 41)	P,2

172

Machaerium biovulatum Micheli	P,3
Ormosia cruenta Rudd	PM,3
Pterocarpus rohrii Vahl, cf.	PMA,3
Styphnolobium monteviridis M. Sousa & Rudd	PM,3
FAGACEAE	
Quercus brenesii Trel.	M,2
corrugata Hook.	MA,3
insignis M. Martens & Galeotti	M,3
seemannii Liebm.	M,3
FLACOURTIACEAE	
Casearia aculeata Jacq.	P,2
corymbosa Kunth	P,1
sylvestris Sw.	PM,2
tacanensis Lundell	M,3
Hasseltia floribunda Kunth	MA,3
Hasseltiopsis dioica (Benth.) Sleumer	M,2
Lozania mutisiana Roem. & Schult.	M,2
Lunania mexicana Brandegee	MA,2
Macrohasseltia macroterantha (Standl. & L. O. Williams) L. O. Williams	MA,3
Prockia crucis P. Browne ex L.	P,1
Xylosma chlorantha Donn. Sm.	M,2
flexuosa (Kunth) Hemsl.	P,1
hispidula Standl.	MA,1
intermedia (Seem.) Triana & Planch.	M,2
oligandra Donn. Sm.	M,2
HERNANDIACEAE	
Gyrocarpus jatrophifolius Domin	P,3
HIPPOCASTANACEAE	
Billia colombiana Planch. & Lindl.	PMA,3
hippocastanum Peyr.	M,3
HIPPOCRATEACEAE	
Salacia petenensis Lundell	MA,2
HYDROPHYLLACEAE	
Wigandia urens (Ruiz & Pav.) Kunth	PM,1
ICACINACEAE	
Calatola costaricensis Standl.	MA,2
JUGLANDACEAE	
Alfaroa costaricensis Standl.	MA,3
williamsii A. R. Molina	M,3
LAURACEAE	
Beilschmiedia brenesii C. K. Allen	PM,3
ovalis (S. F. Blake) C. K. Allen	M,3
pendula (Sw.) Hemsl.	MA,3
near *brenesii* (10749)	M,3
sp. B (11092)	M,3
sp. C (11070)	P,3
Cinnamomum brenesii (Standl.) Kosterm.	P,2

cinnamomifolium (Kunth) Kosterm.	M,3
neurophyllum (Mez & Pittier) Kosterm.	M,3
paratriplinerve Lorea-Hernandez	M,3
Licaria excelsa Kosterm.	MA,3
triandra (Sw.) Kosterm.	PM,3
Nectandra martinicensis Mez	P,2
membranacea (Sw.) Griseb.	MA,3
salicina C. K. Allen	M,3
smithii C. K. Allen	M,2
umbrosa (Kunth) Mez	P,2
Ocotea endresiana Mez	M,3
floribunda (Sw.) Mez	M,3
gomezii W. C. Burger	MA,2
holdridgeiana W. C. Burger, aff. (11093)	M,2
leucoxylon (Sw.) Laness.	PM,3
meziana C. K. Allen	M,3
monteverdensis W. C. Burger	M,3
nicaraguensis Mez	MA,2
paulii C. K. Allen	MA,1
pittieri (Mez) van der Werff	M,2
sinuata (Mez) Rohwer	PM,3
tenera Mez & Donn. Sm. ex Mez	MA,1
tonduzii Standl. (=*insularis*)	MA,3
valeriana (Standl.) W. C. Burger	MA,2
veraguensis (Meisn.) Mez	P,2
viridiflora Lundell, aff. (10876)	M,3
whitei Woodson	PM,3
sp. A "Los Llanos" (11063)	PM,3
sp. B "Tajo" (10808)	M,3
sp. C "Small leaf ira marañon" (11458)	M,3
sp. D "Swamp" (9792)	M,1
Persea americana Mill.	PM,3
caerulea (Ruiz & Pav.) Mez	PM,2
nubigena L. O. Williams, cf.	MA,3
schiedeana Nees	MA,3
veraguasensis Seem.	PM,2
Pleurothyrium palmanum (Mez & Donn. Sm.) Rohwer	MA,3
guindonii van der Werff	M,3
LOGANIACEAE	
Buddleja americana L.	M,1
LORANTHACEAE	
Gaiadendron punctatum (Ruiz & Pav.) G. Don	M,1
MAGNOLIACEAE	
Magnolia poasana (Pittier) Dandy	M,3
Talauma gloriensis Pittier	M,3
MALPIGHIACEAE	
Bunchosia macrophylla Rose	M,1
ocellata Lundell	P,2
ternata Dobson	M,1

174

veluticarpa W. R. Anderson	MA,3
Byrsonima crassifolia (L.) Kunth	P,2
Malpighia albiflora (Cuatrec.) Cuatrec.	MA,1
glabra L.	PM,1
MALVACEAE	
Hampea appendiculata (Donn. Sm.) Standl.	PMA,3
Malvaviscus arboreus Cav.	PMA,1
palmanus Pittier & Donn. Sm.	MA,1
Wercklea insignis Pittier & Standl. ex Standl.	PMA,2
MELASTOMATACEAE	
Conostegia brenesii Standl.	M,1
montana (Sw.) D. Don ex DC.	M,1
oerstediana O. Berg ex Triana	M,1
pittieri Cogn.	M,2
rhodopetala Donn. Sm.	M,1
rufescens Naudin	MA,2
vulcanicola Donn. Sm.	M,1
xalapensis (Bonpl.) D. Don	PM,2
Graffenrieda micrantha (Gleason) L. O. Williams	M,1
Meriania phlomoides (Triana) Almeda	M,1
Miconia amplinodis Umaña & Almeda	M,1
argentea (Sw.) DC.	P,2
brenesii Standl.	MA,1
costaricensis Cogn.	M,1
cuspidatissima Pittier	M,1
dolichopoda Naudin	M,2
donlana Naudin	MA,2
globuliflora (Rich.) Cogn.	M,1
gracilis Triana	MA,1
lonchophylla Naudin	M,1
tonduzii Cogn.	M,1
sp. A "TV Tower" (10283)	M,2
Mouriri exilis Gleason	M,3
Ossaea micrantha (Sw.) Macfad.	MA,1
Topobea brenesii Standl. (hemi-epiphyte)	M,1
maurofernandeziana Cogn. (hemi-epiphyte)	MA,1
pittieri Cogn. (hemi-epiphyte)	M,1
MELIACEAE	
Cedrela salvadorensis Standl.	P,3
tonduzii C. DC.	MA,3
Guarea glabra Vahl	PMA,2
kunthiana A. Juss.	MA,3
rhopalocarpa Radlk.	PMA,3
tonduzii C. DC.	M,2
Ruagea glabra Triana & Planch.	M,3
Trichilia glabra L.	P,3
havanensis Jacq.	PMA,3
martiana C. DC.	PA,2

175

MONIMIACEAE
Mollinedia pinchotiana Perkins · · · M,1
   sp. A (10573) · · · M,1
Siparuna andina (Tul.) A. DC. · · · M,1
   guianensis Aubl. · · · MA,1
   macra Standl. · · · M,1
   tonduziana Perkins · · · MA,1

MORACEAE
Brosimum alicastrum Sw. · · · P,3
Clarisia biflora Ruiz & Pav.. · · · P,3
Ficus citrifolia Mill. · · · P,3
   costaricana (Liebm.) Miq. · · · P,3
   crassiuscula Warb. ex Standl. · · · MA,3
   hartwegii (Miq.) Miq. · · · MA,3
   macbridei Standl. · · · M,2
   obtusifolia Kunth · · · P,3
   pertusa L. f. · · · MA,2
   tuerckheimii Standl. · · · M,3
   trachelosyce Dugand · · · P,2
   velutina Willd. · · · MA,2
   yoponensis Desv. · · · PM,3
Maclura tinctoria (L.) G. Don · · · P,3
Pseudolmedia mollis Standl. · · · MA,3
   spuria (Sw.) Griseb. · · · P,3
Sorocea trophoides W. C. Burger · · · MA,2
Trophis mexicana (Liebm.) Bureau · · · M,2
   racemosa (L.) Urb. · · · P,2

MYRICACEAE
Myrica cerifera L. · · · P,1
   phanerodonta Standl. · · · M,1

MYRSINACEAE
Ardisia compressa Kunth · · · PMA,1
   palmana Donn. Sm. · · · MA,2
   revoluta Kunth · · · P,1
   solomonii (Lundell) Pipoly · · · M,2
Myrsine coriacea (Sw.) R. Br. ex Roem. & Schult. · · · M2
Parathesis glabra Donn. Sm. · · · M,2
   sp. A "Tract X" (10801) · · · M,2

MYRTACEAE
Calyptranthes monteverdensis P. E. Sánchez, ined. · · · M,2
   pallens Griseb. · · · P,2
   pittieri Standl. · · · M,3
Eugenia acapulcensis Steud. · · · P,2
   austin-smithii Standl. · · · M,2
   costaricensis O. Berg · · · M,2
   guatemalensis Donn. Sm. · · · M,3
   haberi P. E. Sánchez, ined. · · · M,2
   monticola (Sw.) DC. · · · M,2
   octopleura Krug & Urb. ex Urb. · · · M,3

oerstediana O. Berg	M,2
salamensis Donn. Sm.	P,2
valerii Standl.	MA,2
Myrcia mollis (Kunth) DC.	M,3
splendens (Sw.) DC.	M,2
sp. A "Fuzzy leaf" (9897)	M,2
Myrcianthes fragrans (Sw.) McVaugh	M,3
sp. A "Black fruit" (297)	PM,3
Psidium guajava L.	PMA,2
sartorianum (O. Berg) Nied.	P,2
sp. A "Cerro Amigos" (11464)	M,3

NYCTAGINACEAE

Neea psychotrioides Donn. Sm.	PM,1
sp. A "Red vein" (1008)	MA,1
sp. B "San Luis" (Bello 37)	P,2
Pisonia sylvatica Standl.	M,1

OCHNACEAE

Ouratea lucens (Kunth) Engl.	P,2

OLACACEAE

Heisteria acuminata (Humb. & Bonpl.) Engl.	PM,1

OLEACEAE

Chionanthus panamensis (Standl.) Stearn	M,3
Forestiera cartaginense Donn. Sm.	P,1

ONAGRACEAE

Hauya lucida Donn. Sm. & Rose	P,2

PAPAVERACEAE

Bocconia frutescens L.	MA,1

PIPERACEAE

Piper amalago L.	M,1
auritum Kunth	M,1
imperiale (Miq.) C. DC.	M,1

PODOCARPACEAE

Podocarpus monteverdeensis de Laub.	M,3

POLYGONACEAE

Triplaris malaenodendron (Bertol.) Standl. & Steyerm.	P,2

PROTEACEAE

Panopsis suaveolens (Klotzsch & H. Karst.) Pittier	M,3
Roupala glaberrima Pittier	M,3
montana Aubl.	P,1

RHAMNACEAE

Rhamnus sphaerosperma Sw.	M,2

RHIZOPHORACEAE

Cassipourea elliptica (Sw.) Poit.	MA,2

ROSACEAE

Prunus annularis Koehne	M,2
cornifolia Koehne	MA,2
sp. A "Big leaf" (440)	PMA,3

sp. B "Bajo Tigre" (11419)	M,2
RUBIACEAE	
Chiococca pachyphylla Wernham	PM,1
Chione sylvicola (Standl.) W. C. Burger	MA,3
Cosmibuena grandiflora (Ruiz & Pav.) Rusby	P,2
valerii (Standl.) C. M. Taylor	M,2
Coussarea austin-smithii Standl.	M,1
caroliana Standl.	P,1
chiriquiensis (Dwyer) C. M. Taylor	M,1
Elaeagia auriculata Hemsl.	MA,2
Faramea multiflora A. Rich.	M,1
occidentalis (L.) A. Rich.	P,2
ovalis Standl.	M,1
Gonzalagunia panamensis (Cav.) K. Schum.	P,1
rosea Standl.	PMA,1
Guettarda poasana Standl.	MA,2
tournefortiopsis Standl.	M,1
Hamelia patens Jacq.	PM,1
Ladenbergia brenesii Standl.	M,2
valerii Standl.	MA,2
Palicourea albocaerulea C. M. Taylor	M,1
montivaga Standl.	M,1
padifolia (Roem. & Schult.) C. M. Taylor & Lorence	M,1
tilaranensis C. M. Taylor	M,1
Posoqueria latifolia (Rudge) Roem. & Schult.	MA,2
Psychotria elata (Sw.) Hammel	MA,1
eurycarpa Standl.	MA,1
horizontalis Sw.	M,1
jimenezii Standl.	M,1
monteverdensis Dwyer & C. W. Ham.	M,1
panamensis Standl.	M,1
sarapiquensis Standl.	M,1
valeriana Standl.	MA,1
sp. A "Long petiole" (10590)	PM,1
Randia brenesii Standl.	MA,2
calycosa Standl.	P,1
matudae Lorence & Dwyer	M,2
monantha Benth.	PM,1
sp. A "Bullpen" (9753)	M,2
Rondeletia amoena (Planch.) Hemsl.	M,1
aspera Standl.	PM,2
brenesii Standl.	PMA,2
buddleioides Benth.	MA,2
monteverdensis Lorence	M,1
torresii Standl.	MA,1
Sommera donnell-smithii Standl.	PMA,1
RUTACEAE	
Amyris balsamifera L.	P,1
Casimiroa edulis La Llave & Lex.	M,3

Peltostigma guatemalense (Standl. & Steyerm.) Gereau, ined.	PMA,1
Stauranthus perforatus Liebm.	M,2
Zanthoxylum fagara (L.) Sarg.	PM,2
melanostictum Schltdl. & Cham.	M,2
monophyllum (Lam.) P. Wilson	PM,2
juniperinum Poepp.	PMA,1
setulosum P. Wilson	P,3
SABIACEAE	
Meliosma idiopoda S. F. Blake	PMA,2
subcordata Standl.	M,2
vernicosa (Liebm.) Griseb.	MA,3
SAPINDACEAE	
Allophylus occidentalis (Sw.) Radlk.	P,2
Cupania glabra Sw.	M,3
guatemalensis (Turcz.) Radlk.	P,2
macrophylla A. Rich.	MA,3
Dilodendron costaricense (Radlk.) A. H. Gentry & Steyerm.	P,3
Exothea paniculata (Juss.) Radlk.	PM,3
Matayba oppositifolia (A. Rich.) Britton	M,3
sp. A "Teton" (9775)	M,3
SAPOTACEAE	
Chrysophyllum brenesii Cronquist	P,3
Manilkara chicle (Pittier) Gilly	P,3
Pouteria exfoliata T. D. Penn.	M,3
fossicola Cronquist	MA,3
reticulata (Engl.) Eyma	MA,3
Sideroxylon capiri (A. DC.) Pittier	P,3
persimile (Hemsl.) T. D. Penn.	P,2
stenospermum (Standl.) T. D. Penn.	M,3
SIMAROUBACEAE	
Picramnia antidesma Sw.	P,1
teapensis Tul.	M,1
sp. A "Cliff edge" (9242)	M,1
sp. B "Cloud forest" (10974)	M,1
Picrasma excelsa (Sw.) Planch.	M,2
SOLANACEAE	
Acnistus arborescens (L.) Schltdl.	PM,2
Cestrum fragile Francey	M,1
lanatum M. Martens & Galeotti	PM,2
megalophyllum Dunal	MA,1
racemosum Ruiz & Pav.	MA,1
rugulosum Francey	M,1
sp. A "Button berry" (11365)	M,1
sp. B "Blue flower" (11209)	M,1
Cuatresia exiguiflora (D'Arcy) Hunz.	M,1
riparia (Kunth) Hunz.	PMA,1
Solanum accrescens Standl. & C. V. Morton	M,1
aphyodendron S. Knapp	PMA,1

179

argenteum Dunal ex Poir.	MA,1
brenesii Standl.	PM,1
chrysotrichum Schltdl.	MA,1
cordovense Sessé & Mociño	M,1
pastillum S. Knapp	M,1
rovirosanum Donn. Sm.	PMA,1
rudepannum Dunal	PMA,1
umbellatum Mill.	M,1
Witheringia cuneata (Standl.) Hunz.	PM,1

STAPHYLEACEAE
Turpinia occidentalis (Sw.) G. Don	MA,2

STERCULIACEAE
Guazuma ulmifolia Lam.	P,2

STYRACACEAE
Styrax argenteus C. Presl	PM,3
conterminus Donn. Sm.	M,2
glabrescens Benth.	MA,2

SYMPLOCACEAE
Symplocos brenesii Standl.	M,3
costaricana Hemsl.	MA,3
limoncillo Humb. & Bonpl.	M,3
povedae Almeda	M,1
tribracteolata Almeda	M,3

THEACEAE
Cleyera theioides (Sw.) Choisy	M,2
Freziera candicans Tul.	M,2
friedrichsthaliana (Szyszyl.) Kobuski	M,2
Gordonia brandegeei H. Keng	M,3
Symplococarpon purpusii (Brandegee) Kobuski	M,3
Ternstroemia tepezapote Schltdl. & Cham.	M,3

THYMELAEACEAE
Daphnopsis americana (Mill.) J. R. Johnst.	PM,3

TICODENDRACEAE
Ticodendron incognitum Gómez-Laur. & L. D. Gómez	MA 2

TILIACEAE
Heliocarpus americanus L.	MA,2
appendiculatus Turcz.	P,2
Luehea speciosa Willd.	P,2
Mortoniodendron costaricense Standl. & L. O. Williams	M,2
guatemalense Standl. & Steyerm.	M,2
Triumfetta calderonii Standl.	P,1

ULMACEAE
Trema micrantha (L.) Blume	PMA,2
Ulmus mexicana (Liebm.) Planch.	PM,3

URTICACEAE
Discocnide mexicana (Liebm.) Chew	P,1
Myriocarpa bifurca Liebm.	P,1
cordifolia Liebm.	M,1

longipes Liebm.	MA,1
Phenax mexicanus Wedd.	P,1
Urera baccifera (L.) Gaudich.	P,2
caracasana (Jacq.) Griseb.	PMA,1
corallina (Liebm.) Wedd.	P,1
elata (Sw.) Griseb.	MA,1
near *elata* (9294)	PM,1
VERBENACEAE	
Aegiphila anomala Pittier	P,2
odontophylla Donn. Sm.	M,1
valerii Standl.	PM,2
Citharexylum caudatum L.	MA,3
costaricensis Moldenke	M,2
donnell-smithii Greenm.	MA,3
Cornutia grandiflora (Schltdl. & Cham.) Schauer	MA,2
WINTERACEAE	
Drimys granadensis L. f.	M,2

* = introduced species sometimes found outside of cultivation.

CULTIVATED SPECIES

Annonaceae, *Annona cherimola* Mill., "Custard apple, *Anona, Cherimoya*"
Apocynaceae, *Thevetia peruviana* (Pers.) K. Schum., "Yellow oleander"
Araucariaceae, *Araucaria araucana* (Molina) K. Koch, "Monkey puzzle"
    Araucaria heterophylla, "Norfolk Island pine"
Betulaceae, *Alnus acuminata* Kunth, "Alder, *Jaúl*"
Caricaceae, *Carica papaya* L., "Papaya"
Casuarinaceae, *Casuarina equisetifolia* J. R. Forst., "Whistling pine"
Clusiaceae, *Clusia stenophylla* Standl., "Clusia, *Azahar de monte, Copey*"
Cupressaceae, *Cupressus lusitanica* Mill., "Mexican cypress, *Ciprés*"
Euphorbiaceae, *Cnidoscolus aconitifolius* (Mill.) I. M. Johnst., "*Chicasquil*"
    Croton niveus Jacq., "*Colpachí*"
Fabaceae (Mimosoideae), *Calliandra* sp., "Powderpuff, *Carboncillo*"
Juglandaceae, *Juglans olanchana* Standl. & L. O. Williams, "Walnut, *Nogal*"
Moraceae, *Ficus goldmanii* Standl.
    Ficus pertusa L. f. "*Higuillo*"
Myrtaceae, *Eucalyptus deglupta* Blume and other spp., "Eucalyptus, *Eucalypto*"
    Eugenia uniflora L., "Surinam cherry"
    Psidium guajava L., "Guava, *Guayaba*"
    Syzygium jambos (L.) Alston, "Rose apple, *Manzana rosa*"
        malaccense (L.) Merr. & L. M. Perry, "Malay apple, *Manzana de agua*"
Oleaceae, *Fraxinus uhdei* (Wenz.) Lingelsh., "Tropical ash, *Fresno*"
    Ligustrum sp., "Privet, *Trueno*"
Pinaceae, *Pinus caribaea* Morelet, "Caribbean pine, *Pino*"
Rosaceae, *Eriobotrya japonica* (Thunb.) Lindl., "Loquat, *Nispero*"
Rubiaceae, *Coffea arabica* L. "Coffee, *Café*"
Rutaceae, *Citrus aurantium* L., "Sour orange, *Naranja agria*"
Verbenaceae, *Duranta erecta* L., "Golden dewdrop"

APPENDIX 3.
TREES GROUPED BY SOME OF THEIR NOTABLE CHARACTERISTICS

A. Largest Trees

Cloud forest

Beilschmiedia pendula
Dussia sp.
Ficus crassiuscula
F. hartwegii
Gordonia brandegeei
Ocotea tonduzii
Persea schiedeana
Pouteria fossicola
Quercus corrugata
Sapium rigidifolium

Pacific slope forest

Billia colombiana
Bourreria costaricensis
Cedrela tonduzii
Ficus tuerckheimii
Ocotea whitei
Panopsis suaveolens
Pouteria exfoliata
Quercus insignis
Roupala glaberrima
Sideroxylon stenospermum

B. Second growth trees found in pastures

Cloud forest

Bocconia frutescens
Cecropia polyphlebia
Conostegia oerstediana
Guettarda poasana
Hampea appendiculata
Heliocarpus americanus
Myrsine coriacea
Neomirandea angularis
Rondeletia monteverdensis
Saurauia montana
Trema micrantha
Urera elata

Pacific slope forest

Acnistus arborescens
Cecropia obtusifolia
Citharexylum costaricensis
Clethra lanata
Conostegia xalapensis
Croton monteverdensis
Daphnopsis americana
Inga sierrae & punctata
Myrsine coriacea
Oreopanax xalapensis
Piper auritum
Psidium guajava
Solanum aphyodendron &
S. umbellatum
Trema micrantha
Urera caracasana
Viburnum costaricanum
Xylosma chlorantha
Zanthoxylum fagara

C. Trees with milky or colored latex

Bocconia frutescens (watery orange sap)
Clusia spp. (yellow, white or clear)
Croton draco (red)
Ficus spp. (white)
Garcinia intermedia (yellow)
Hampea appendiculata (watery yellow)
Pouteria spp. (white)
Sapium spp. (white)
Sideroxylon stenospermum (white)
Stemmadenia spp. (white)
Symphonia globulifera (yellow)
Tabernaemontana longipes (white)
Tovomitopsis spp. (white)

D. Trees with large fruits ("edible"= eaten by seed dispersers)

Amphitecna haberi & *A. isthmica* (edible seed pulp, hard shell)
Billia colombiana (leathery husk, naked seed)
Bourreria costaricensis (fleshy rind)
Capparis discolor (arillate seeds)
Casimiroa edulis (fleshy rind)
Casearia tacanensis (leathery husk, edible seed pulp)
Ficus crassiuscula (whole fruit eaten)
Guarea kunthiana (arillate seeds)
Magnolia poasana (arillate seeds)
Panopsis suaveolens (woody shell, naked seed)
Persea americana (edible rind)
P. schiedeana (edible rind)
Piper spp. (whole fruit edible)
Pouteria fossicola (edible rind)
Randia matudae (edible seed pulp)
Salacia petenensis (edible jelly around seeds)
Sloanea ampla (arillate seeds)
Stemmadenia litoralis (arillate seeds)

E. Trees with elongate fruits or pods

Capparis cynophallophora & *pringlei* (long bean-like pod with arillate seeds)
Cecropia obtusifolia (elongate fleshy fruit with small seeds)
Dussia sp. (pod with arillate seeds)
Erythrina lanceolata (elongate pod with several red seeds)
Inga spp. (pod with large arillate seeds)
Ormosia cruenta (pod with 1-2 red seeds)
Piper auritum (elongate fleshy spike with tiny seeds)
Pithecellobium costaricense (*Cojoba costaricensis*) (elongate pod, black seeds)
P. palmanum (*Zygia palmana*) (flat pod with large brown seeds)
Roupala glaberrima (pod with two winged seeds)
Styphnolobium monteviridis (indehiscent pod with 1-3 seeds)

F. Trees with dehiscing capsules

Alchornea latifolia (seeds arillate)
Bocconia frutescens (arillate)
Casearia sylvestris (arillate)
Cedrela tonduzii (winged)
Clethra spp. (tiny wind-borne seeds)
Clusia spp. (arillate)
Croton monteverdensis (explosive)
Cupania glabra (arillate)
Elaeagia auriculata (minute wind-borne seeds)
Gordonia brandegeei (winged)
Guarea spp. (arillate)
Gymnosporia haberiana (arillate)
Hampea appendiculata (arillate)
Magnolia poasana (arillate)
Matayba spp. (arillate)
Maytenus spp. (arillate)
Rondeletia spp. (tiny wind-borne seeds)
Ruagea glabra (arillate)
Sapium spp. (arillate)
Saurauia montana (seeds in a soft edible matrix)
Siparuna spp. (arillate)
Sloanea spp. (arillate)
Stemmadenia litoralis (arillate)
Tabernaemontana longipes (arillate)
Ternstroemia tepezapote (arillate)
Tetrorchidium spp. (arillate)
Trichilia spp. (arillate)
Zanthoxylum spp. (hard seeds with oily coating)

G. Trees with wind-borne seeds

Asteraceae (most species)
Cedrela tonduzii
Clethra lanata
Elaeagia auriculata
Gordonia brandegeei
Heliocarpus spp.
Rondeletia spp.
Roupala glaberrima

H. Trees with mammal dispersed fruits (the part eaten in parentheses)

Amphitecna spp. (seed matrix)
Billia spp. (seed)
Bourreria costaricensis (rind)
Cecropia spp. (also birds—all)
Conostegia oerstediana (also birds—all)
Eugenia guatemalensis (soft rind)
Ficus crassiuscula (all)
Inga spp. (aril)
Meliosma vernicosa (rind)
Panopsis suaveolens (seed)
Persea americana (soft rind)
P. schiedeana (soft rind)
Piper spp. (especially bats- all)
Pouteria fossicola (soft rind, monkeys; seed—agoutis)
Randia matudae (seed matrix)
Quararibea costaricensis (soft rind)
Salacia petenensis (jam-like pulp)
Styphnolobium monteviridis (jelly-like goop surrounding seed)
Ticodendron incognitum (rind)

I. Trees with spines

Bactris spp. (long needle-like spines on trunk and leaves)
Erythrina lanceolata (hooked spines on trunk, branches and leaves)
Pisonia sylvatica (short spines on twigs)
Randia spp. (short, paired spines on twigs)
Xylosma spp. (branched spines on trunk)
Zanthoxylum spp. (conical spines on trunk)

J. Tree families with translucent yellow dots (oil glands) in leaves

Flacourtiaceae (some species of *Casearia*)
Myrsinaceae (yellow or red dots and streaks)
Myrtaceae (yellow dots)
Rutaceae (yellow dots, at least along leaf margin)

K. Tree families with distinctive leaf odors

Annonaceae (weak aromatic oils)
Fabaceae (string bean)
Lauraceae (aromatic oils)
Myrtaceae (aromatic oils)
Piperaceae (spicy)
Rosaceae (bitter almond)
Rutaceae (citrus)
Solanaceae (bitter or rank)

APPENDIX 4.
GLOSSARY OF BOTANICAL TERMS

achene: dry, indehiscent fruit with a single seed, such as in many Asteraceae and Urticaceae.

adventitious: produced from an unusual position.

alternate: with one leaf (or flower, bract, etc.) per node.

anther: bulging apical part of the stamen that contains the pollen.

apex: tip or end, the part furthest from base, e.g., a leaf apex.

aril: fleshy, edible tissue, often brightly colored, attached at the base of a seed. Usually found in capsular fruits.

axil: upper angle between the petiole and the stem.

berry: soft, indehiscent fruit containing few to numerous seeds, usually eaten as a unit by seed-dispersing animals.

bisexual: flower containing both male parts (stamens, anthers and pollen) and female parts (ovary, style and stigma).

blade: broad, flat part of a leaf or leaflet, the lamina.

bract: usually small, leaf-like or scale-like structure associated with inflorescences, often beneath or surrounding flowers or at branching points of the inflorescence.

calyx: outer whorl of floral parts below the corolla, often with marginal lobes called sepals.

capsule: dry fruit composed of several cells that opens into several valves when mature by dehiscing along regular suture lines; usually containing several to many seeds and these often bear an aril.

compound leaf: a leaf divided into distinct, leaf-like segments called leaflets that are separated to the base. Compound leaves usually have a distinct petiole with swollen base (pulvinus) and lack buds at the tip of the rachis and in the axils of the leaflets.

corolla: attractive whorl of flower parts above the calyx, usually with several lobes on the margin called petals when they are distinct from each other.

crownshaft: smooth area at the stem apex of some palms formed by the overlapping petioles that enwrap the stem.

cupule: cup-like structure surrounding the base of some fruits, e.g., Lauraceae.

deciduous: falling away at the end of a growth period, e.g., trees that drop their leaves in the dry season.

dehiscence: the normal process by which capsular fruits or anthers split open at maturity to expose their seeds or pollen.

dioecious: species that contain individuals of only one functional sex, e.g., male or female. The flowers of a given individual are unisexual and of only one kind—male or female.

diurnal: active during daylight hours, e.g., flowers that open and produce nectar and scent during the day.

drupe: a fleshy, one-seeded fruit that does not dehisce.

entire: margin without teeth.

epiphyte: a plant that grows rooted on another plant, for example many orchids and bromeliads. Note that epiphytic plants also occasionally grow on rocks, tree stumps,

186

logs and cut road banks, while terrestrial species sometimes grow like epiphytes on logs and tree trunks.

extrafloral nectary: a nectar-secreting gland occurring outside a flower; produces nectar as an attractant for ants that guard the plant from herbivores. Extrafloral nectaries range from a small spot on a leaf blade (e.g., *Prunus*) to a distinctive gland on a narrow stalk (e.g., *Croton, Inga*, and *Sapium*).

glabrous: lacking hairs or pubescence.

hemi-epiphyte: a plant that begins life as an epiphyte, but sends roots to the ground as it grows in order to take up water and nutrients from the soil (e.g., *Clusia, Ficus*).

heterostylous: having two or three different flower style lengths in various individuals of the same species.

inferior ovary: an ovary submerged in the flower base below the attachment point of the sepals and petals (e.g., Melastomataceae, Myrtaceae, Rubiaceae).

inflorescence: the reproductive part of the plant bearing the flowers, often a branched structure with numerous flowers.

infructescence: the fruit-bearing structure of the plant.

internode: the part of a stem or twig between two adjoining nodes.

interpetiolar: between the leaf stems (petioles).

intrapetiolar: in the axil of the leaf stem (petiole).

lateral veins: the group of secondary veins usually branching off from the midvein or radiating from the leaf base.

latex: milky or colored liquid exuded from cuts in plant tissue.

leaflet: one of the individual leaf-like units that make up a compound leaf.

meristem: the active, growing tissue at the tip of a stem.

midvein: the central, main vein of a leaf or leaflet; midrib.

monoecious: a plant species in which each individual produces both male and female flowers, that is unisexual flowers of both sexes.

nocturnal: flowers or pollinators that are behaviorally active during the hours of darkness, e.g., hawk moths and *Cosmibuena* flowers.

node: the point on a stem or twig where leaves are attached.

obovate: egg-shaped, but with the broader end away from the base.

oil glands: minute, translucent dots in leaf tissue that contain aromatic oils, usually thought to be an herbivore deterrent. Found in most species of Myrtaceae and Rutaceae.

opposite: when each node has two leaves, one attached on each side of the stem (can also apply to bracts, flowers, etc.).

ovary: the basal, usually rounded part of the pistil (female part of the flower), containing the ovules or undeveloped seeds, that will develop into a fruit.

palmate: divided into several lobes or separate leaflets attached at one point like the spokes of a wheel or the palm of a hand; digitate. Also, leaf venation of this pattern.

pellucid: appearing translucent when back lit.

petal: the term for the lobes of the corolla when they are separate from each other; the petals are usually the most colorful and attractive part of the flower.

petiole: the leaf stalk that supports a leaf blade and connects it to the node.

pinna, (plural: **pinnae**): the separate leaflets of the compound leaf of a palm.

pinnate: with four or more leaflets arranged in two rows along the rachis. Also applies to venation arranged in this pattern.

pubescent: coated with hairs or fuzz, i.e., a pubescent leaf.

pulvinus: the swollen base or tip of a petiole characteristic of many compound leaves.

rachis: the midvein of a pinnate leaf, attached at the tip of the petiole.

sap: watery liquid exuded from a cut in the bark, twigs or leaves of a living plant; called latex when it is milky or colored.

sepal: one of the lobes of the calyx when these are distinct from each other; the sepals are usually green and leaflike.

simple leaf: a leaf with the blade not divided into separate segments. Although it may be deeply toothed or lobed, the divisions do not reach to the midvein.

spathe: a large bract that surrounds an inflorescence, e.g., in palms.

stamen: the male or staminate part of a flower, consisting of the filament or stalk and the anther or pollen-producing sac.

stellate: starlike, e.g., stellate hairs of Malvaceae and Tiliaceae.

stipule: a small, scale-like or leaf-like structure associated with a leaf and attached near the base of the petiole; a leaf may have one or a pair of stipules or none; most easily seen on new growth because they are often deciduous.

strangler: some species of figs (*Ficus* spp.) that begin growing as epiphytes, but later produce adventitious roots that coalesce to form a woody trunk around the host tree. The constriction of the host's trunk along with shading of its crown eventually kills the host leaving the fig as a self-supporting tree.

sympatric: two species occurring in the same place; having overlapping distributions.

style: one or more usually slender stalks attached at the tip of the ovary that bear the stigma (pollen-collecting tissue) at their tips.

superior ovary: an ovary attached above the calyx and corolla and standing free from them.

tepal: term for a petal or sepal of a flower when these two parts are similar in appearance.

translucent dots: oil glands inside leaf tissue that can be seen when holding a leaf blade up to strong light; characteristic of certain plant families such as Myrtaceae, Myrsinaceae and Rutaceae (see oil glands).

trifoliolate: with three leaflets.

trunk: the woody, main stem of a tree or treelet.

umbel: an inflorescence in which flower stems all radiate from a central point.

unisexual: describing flowers that contain the functional parts of only one sex, either male (staminate) or female (pistillate). The flowers of many dioecious species are unisexual in function, but bear the reduced and non-functional parts of the opposite sex.

whorled: with three or more leaves at a node, e.g., *Viburnum costaricanum*.

APPENDIX 5.
SOME REFERENCES AND RESOURCES USED IN PREPARING THIS BOOK
THAT MAY BE HELPFUL FOR STUDYING COSTA RICAN TREES

Allen, P.H. 1956. *The Rain Forests of Golfo Dulce.* Stanford University Press (reprinted 1977), Stanford.

Bolaños, R.A. and V. Watson. 1993. *Mapa Ecológico de Costa Rica.* Centro Científico Tropical, San José, Costa Rica.

Burger, W. and H. van der Werff. 1990. Family #80. Lauraceae. In: *Fieldiana: Botany.* Field Museum of Natural History, Chicago.

Croat, T.B. 1978. *Flora of Barro Colorado Island.* Stanford University Press, Stanford.

Cronquist, A. 1981. *An Integrated System of Classification of Flowering Plants.* Columbia University Press, New York.

Flora Costaricensis, W. Burger , ed. *Fieldiana: Botany.* (Continuing series in various volumes and New Series). Field Museum of Natural History, Chicago.

Flora of Panama. 1943–1980. R.E. Woodson and R.W. Schery, editors. *Annals Missouri Bot. Gard.* (appearing in many volumes).

Fournier, L.O., E. Flores, D. Rivera. 1985. *Flora Arborescente del Valle Central de Costa Rica.* San José, Costa Rica.

Gentry, A. H. 1993. *A Field Guide to the Families and Genera of Woody Plants of Northwest South America.* Conservation International, Washington, D.C.

Haber, W.A. 1990. Lista provisional de las plantas de Monteverde, Costa Rica. *Brenesia* No. 34: 63–120.

Hartshorn, G.S. 1983. Plants, Introduction. In: *Costa Rican Natural History*, D.H. Janzen, ed. Univ. of Chicago Press, Chicago.

Hartshorn, G.S. and B.A. Hammel. 1994. Vegetation types and floristic patterns. In: *La Selva: Ecology and Natural History of a Neotropical Rain Forest.* McDade, L.A., K.S. Bawa, H.A. Hespenheide and G.S. Hartshorn, eds. Univ. of Chicago Press, Chicago.

Heywood, V.H. 1985. *Flowering Plants of the World.* Prentice Hall, Inc., Englewood Cliffs, N.J.

Holdridge, L. 1967. *Life Zone Ecology.* Tropical Science Center, San Jose, Costa Rica.

Holdridge, L.R. and L.J. Poveda. 1975. *Arboles de Costa Rica. Volumen 1. Palmas, otras monocotyledoneas Arboreas y Arboles con Hojas Compuestas o Lobuladas.* Centro Científico Tropical, San José, Costa Rica.

Instituto Nacional de Biodiversidad Internet site: http://www.inbio.ac.cr/manual.plantas/plantae.html

190

Janzen, D.H., editor. 1983. *Costa Rican Natural History.* University of Chicago Press, Chicago, USA.

Kappelle, M., N. Zamora, and T. Flores. 1990. Flora leñosa de la zona alta (2000–3819 m) de la Cordillera de Talamanca, Costa Rica. *Brenesia* No. 34: 121–144.

Lawton, R. and V. Dryer. 1980. The vegetation of the Monteverde Cloud Forest Reserve. *Brenesia* No. 18: 101–116.

Mabberley, D.J. 1987. *The Plant Book, A Portable Dictionary of Higher Plants.* Cambridge University Press, Cambridge, England.

Nadkarni, N. and N. Wheelwright, eds. 1997. *The Natural History, Ecology and Conservation of Monteverde, Costa Rica.* Oxford University Press, Oxford.

Nadkarni, N., T.J. Matelson, and W.A. Haber. 1995. Structural characteristics and floristic composition of a neotropical cloud forest, Monteverde, Costa Rica. *J. Tropical Ecol.* 11: 481–495.

Niembro, A. 1990. *Arboles y Arbustos Utiles de México.* Editorial Limusa, México D.F., México.

Pennington, T.D. and J. Sarukhan. 1968. *Arboles Tropicales de México.* Instituto Nacional de Investigaciones Forestales, México D.F., México.

Pittier, H. 1978 (reprint). *Plantas Usuales de Costa Rica.* Editorial Costa Rica, San José, Costa Rica.

Standley, P.C. 1937. *Flora of Costa Rica.* Field Museum of Natural History, Botanical Series. Volume 18.

Standley, P.C. and J.A. Steyermark. 1946–1966. *Flora of Guatemala.*

Tosi, J.A. 1969. Mapa Ecológico. Centro Científico Tropical, San José, Costa Rica.

Wheelwright, N.T., W.A. Haber, K.G. Murray, and C. Guindon. 1984. Tropical fruit-eating birds and their food plants: a survey of a Costa Rican lower montane forest. *Biotropica* 16: 173–192.

Zamora, N. 1989. *Flora Arborescente de Costa Rica. 1. Especies de Hojas Simples.* Editorial Tecnológica de Costa Rica, Cartago, Costa Rica.

Zomlefer, Wendy B. 1994. *Guide to Flowering Plant Families.* The University of North Carolina Press, Chapel Hill.

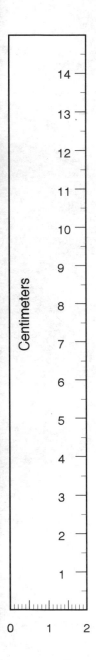

Centimeters